You will also be interested in a distinguished and beautiful edition of

W. H. HUDSON'S

GREEN MANSIONS

with 13 pages in full color and 22 black-and-white headpieces by the Argentine artist, Horacio Butler. Typography and binding design by Rudolph Ruzicka.

THIS IS A BORZOI BOOK PUBLISHED IN NEW YORK BY ALFRED A. KNOPF

THE SHIP OF FLAME

THE SHIP OF FLAME

A SAGA OF THE SOUTH SEAS

By WILLIAM S. STONE

ILLUSTRATED BY NICOLAS MORDVINOFF

NEW YORK

ALFRED A. KNOPF

1945

MANUFACTURED IN THE UNITED STATES OF AMERICA

PUBLISHED SIMULTANEOUSLY IN CANADA BY THE RYERSON PRESS

First and second printings before publication

TO BARBARA

FOREWORD: TETUA* THE TELLER OF TALES

THERE is a strange compulsion in Tetua's very presence which invariably sends a man's thoughts swinging back to the days when Tahiti, undiscovered and unknown by those whose skins are white, was in its glory; to the days when the old gods still looked down on an island world in which great stone temples towered skyward, where warriors, magicians and brave heroes trod the jungle paths and sailed the lonely seas. Possibly it is because Tetua, descended of a line of ancient kings, is himself of the breed of heroes. Although his hair is grayed, his years many, he stands well over six feet tall, his brown body supple and clean-limbed as that of a youth of twenty. Today, of course, he does not rule, yet such is his air of calm and of authority, such the quiet nobility of his even features, that imagination leaps to clothe him in the magnificent regalia of his chieftain ancestors: the mantle of brilliant yellow parakeet feathers draped across his powerful shoulders, the fine white tapa cloth of royalty about his loins, the splendidly plumed war helmet rising above his proud, dark head.

Tetua's home is remote from the nearest settlement, and the way to go is by canoe. It is a pleasant passage, which may be made, if trades are not too boisterous, in about three hours' time, and it leads through a succession of placid lagoons, past sleepily uninspired districts dotted with small homes and coconut plantations; a friendly countryside, pretty and unspectacular, shut in—protected. Then comes a last separating peninsula, a slender finger of coral sand carrying the usual freight of swaying palms, and hiding all that lies beyond. There is nothing remarkable in the appearance of the narrow spit of land; many

* In the Tahitian language, consonants are pronounced as in English. Vowels are similar to Spanish or Italian. There are no silent letters.

such promontories, jutting seaward from the irregular coast line, have been passed before. Who shall explain, therefore, the peculiar awareness with which a traveler, even though it be his first pilgrimage to Tetua's door, approaches this final barrier? But so it is.

As the canoe rounds the point and turns to face the wind one has the conviction that he has come, not to a mere physical boundary between two segments of a single island, but to the dividing portals of two worlds, to a watery threshold between two modes of thought, two ways of life. Behind is the present, the new; ahead the old, the past. The familiar, commonplace Tahiti of today fades as does the tremulous, quickly obliterated wake, and the canoe slips forward onto the deep, blue water of the tremendous bay of Matavai where Tetua's world opens, unfolds, expands. Mountains rise high and majestic, their summits wreathed in cloud. Valleys, dark with shade, widen and lengthen till they expose the very heart of the island. The little ripples of the reef-enclosed lagoon give way to a slow, undulating swell which is the breathing of the sea itself. Still far off lies a vast, crescent-shaped beach washed by curling green waves and, almost in the center of the spreading arc, a dwelling. In truth a spacious and airy house built of native woods, of thatch and bamboo, from a distance—dwarfed by the upthrust peaks behind and the limitless vault overhead—it looks insignificant. For Tetua's is a region in which man is small and the gods loom large. Entering it, spirit and fancy soar like the man-of-war birds which, so says he, are but shadows of those same deities. It is a land in which strange ghosts once rode the night winds, in which the blood of human sacrifices stained the mighty altars, a land brought into being and nurtured by giants of the sky and sea.

The tales of old Tetua, last of island bards, spring from this rich soil. They are singing in his blood and brain, the same stories which have passed from father to son through fifty generations of kings and chiefs.

To meet him our canoe is moving backward down the stream of time, far back, hundreds—even a thousand—of years, into the Polynesian past. Not every man will care for such a voyage; some there are who prefer to lose no moment of the harried present with its wealth of useless knowledge and its brittle erudition. But if you are a bit more leisured than such as they, if you are a trifle weary of sophistry and the nimbly intricate devices of modern story-tellers and long to return to times when men's minds were younger, less complex and more forthright, when imagination was not content to toy with small and petty things but reached out to grasp the entire wheeling heavens, and if, finally, you would take pleasure in the simplicity of a race whose words, thoughts, enthusiasms were exuberant as those of lusty children, spontaneous as all nature, fresh as salt wind-borne spray—why, then, come aboard! The canoe holds room for two, so let us paddle on across the swells of Matavai.

Hold fast as we shoot the surf to where Tetua stands, legs braced apart, knee-deep in rushing water with his strong arms outstretched to seize the gunwales and shout his ready welcome. Help us draw the canoe over the black volcanic sands to the shade of a big-leaved purau tree which grows hard by the house.

Now step inside; seat yourself on the cool pandanus mat. Let the island sounds fill full your ears and mind: the rustling of the coco palms high overhead; the faint rattle of dry thatch at sloping eaves; the sigh of wind through bamboo walls; deep murmur of solid seas pounding on a distant reef. And listen, too, as Tetua speaks, for his also is the voice of Tahiti—as much so as is that of surf and wind and drumbeat of the rain. Let him carry you to those distant days when the south sea islands first rose like green jewels from the surrounding waters, to those days when his people walked hand in hand with mystery and wonder and great miracle. Let him tell you a tale which is always young in Tahitian memories, a tale of valor and of heroism: the story of the foremost of island kings, the first of island men. Rata was his name.

THE SHIP OF FLAME

YOUNG RATA'S HEART BEAT SWIFTLY on that June morning. Not because of the weight of breadfruit slung at either end of the pole balanced on his shoulders; not because of the height at which he found himself nor the steepness of the mountain trail down which his bare feet found their way. Other youths might stagger with such a load upon their backs, but Rata's step was light, his handsome head held high. And yet he could feel the pounding there against his ribs, the quick, throbbing pulse which that day held the people of all Tahiti in a common grip—the grip of great excitement.

As he strode on down the narrow path, brush and tall ferns dragged at his long legs, whipped across the firm brown flesh of his naked chest and back, clawed at the strip of beaten bark-cloth wound tightly about his middle. He paid no attention; only when the strings of breadfruit caught on hanging vines did he pause to wrench them free. Not until the trail left the jungle to skirt the brow of a bald-faced

9

cliff did he come to a halt. Standing a foot from the brink, he paused and looked below.

A large village lay sprawled along the shore, a village made of bamboo, of palm fronds and the tough, pointed leaves of pandanus trees. From above, the houses appeared foreshortened and the tall, steeply pitched thatch roofs hid almost completely the dwellings crouched beneath. But the throng of people milling through the streets was clear to be seen. Dark-skinned chiefs and warriors carrying long spears pushed their way past comely bare-breasted women, past scampering children, past common laborers bent beneath burdens of drinking nuts, pigs, fowls and other island produce. All was bustle and movement and the shouts and cries of the leaders drifted up to Rata, causing his grip to tighten on the carrying-pole. Great adventure was in the making there below. Surely it was adventure in which he was to share? So far he'd not dared ask for fear of refusal. But he could not be denied!

He allowed his glance to swerve southward where, apart from the village, stood the massive marae, the temple of Oro most powerful of all the gods. There, too, was feverish activity. Priests watched carefully the fires over which were being cooked offerings of fish and suckling pig and wild banana. Jealously they guarded the stone and sennit idols, the holy relics of the shrine: skulls of long dead chieftains, weapons of early kings, the hair of Hina-in-the-Moon.

On these things Rata's eyes rested, but only briefly. Then they turned to the wide beach where was gathered the greatest crowd of all. The curving shore was lined with an eager multitude, jostling, pushing, pressing forward so that many of those nearest the sea stood in waist-deep water. All attention centered on three swift war canoes which rode to strong hawsers of twisted coco husk upon the gently rising and falling surface of the bay. The sun was high and reflected blindingly from the untroubled water. Yet it was hardly the glaring light which caused Rata's eyes to dim as he gazed down upon the three gallant ships. The two flanking vessels were of medium size, but that in the center was capable of carrying more than a hundred men in its long twin hulls. With what challenge its bows swept upward in long, graceful curve to end in intricately carved and painted figureheads! There was a craft worthy of bearing a fearless king; and for such it was intended. It was the war canoe of King Tumu-nui, whose only son stood on the cliff above with tears of pride in his eyes as they rested on his father's brave flotilla.

The penetrating blast of a conch shell reached the lad's ears. Three times it blew, followed by a loud cheer from the populace. The time was short; he must hurry. He plunged down the trail, the long strings of breadfruit swinging wildly on the pole. When he reached the village a procession of priests was entering from the direction of the marae, walking with slow and measured pace to solemn chant and hollow beat of drum. In double file they came, bearing Oro's fearful image aloft in their midst. Women turned their eyes away and men retreated to a respectful distance as the wizened high priest, Tahua, led on to the strand where a barge waited to receive the idol and to carry it aboard the king's ship.

Rata raced to his house and burst into the large oval dwelling, then stopped abashed. His mother was in his father's arms and he saw that she was weeping. King Tumu-nui stood grave and tall with the helmet of scarlet ura feathers already upon his head. But when he turned to his son his features softened and a smile touched his lips.

"One thing our expedition will not lack is breadfruit," he observed. "How many times have you been to the hills since dawn?"

"Five times, father," said Rata, dropping his burden to the floor.

"No man could have done better." King Tumu-nui released his wife and going to his son placed strong hands upon his shoulders. He opened his mouth to speak, but Rata gave him no opportunity.

"You are not to say farewell!"

"No?" His father stepped back in mild astonishment. "What is the meaning of this?"

"It means," Rata answered boldly, "that I am going with you!"

"Oho!" Tumu-nui laughed, "our young chick fancies himself a warrior grown."

Queen Maemae did not smile. Her eyes were somber as she regarded the earnest and determined figure of her son. What were his years? Seventeen—eighteen? She was not quite sure. But that there was never a youth with such an air of high resolve, never a youth more perfectly the living example of the finest of Tahiti's blood, she would have been unable to deny even had she not been his mother.

"You have just admitted that I do a man's work," Rata persisted. "May a king's son not carry a spear as well as a load of breadfruit?"

11

"In time, Rata," his father answered with a sigh, "in time. You do not understand the dangers that lie before us. A thousand miles of tossing waves stretch between Tahiti and Revareva * where my sister lives. For many years I have longed to visit her and now I go, but although I have paid my respects to the gods, and although Tahua predicts safe passage, untold perils wait for us at sea. Who knows what we may encounter? Will the hunting demon-bird sight our vessels and dive to tear and rend; will the beast-of-heated-flesh rise along our path; will the devouring clam find us within its crushing jaws? These are things no man can say, but this I may tell you: such a voyage is not for striplings."

Tumu-nui had done better to use another word, for in point of fact Rata was no stripling and many, seeing him standing beside his father, would have said that in most things he might well have been the other's match. But the king's mind was preoccupied with other matters and he did not appear aware of the hurt he had caused his son's pride nor of the flush which spread over the youth's well-formed features.

Queen Maemae went quickly to Rata's side and he allowed her to put her arms about him and to draw him close. Her dark hair, which hung free about her shoulders, fell forward touching his face, surrounding him with the fragrance of coconut oil and crushed gardenias.

"May I grow to *twice* the size of other men!" he exclaimed suddenly, bitterly.

She drew his head down against her breast. "It is not that," she said softly. "It is not a question of size. Already . . ." At the sound of rushing air she paused, and a great-winged man-of-war bird flew into the dim interior, wheeled once, then swooped out and upward to disappear again in the heavens.

"Ah," Queen Maemae breathed with eyes grown large, "shadow of Oro, do you bear away my Rata's wish?"

Tumu-nui did not speak and Rata, whose head was still buried in the warmth of his mother's bosom, had seen nothing at all. But at the rattle of a spear against one of the polished wooden pillars which supported the arched doorway, he broke away from the sweet embrace. Two men entered the dwelling.

Iore, brother of the queen, was a tall, bony man of unwarlike mien

* Hiti-au-revareva is the full name; today called Pitcairn.

13

and at the moment his long face wore a solemn, almost doleful expression.

"Well!" Tumu-nui exclaimed, "there is no need for excessive sadness; this parting is not forever."

"As to that," Iore replied soberly, "who can say save the gods and devils of the sea?"

The king turned to the second newcomer, his steersman. "Is all in readiness, Hoa Pahi?"

Hoa Pahi has the literal meaning, "Friend-of-the-Ship"—and certainly no ship or king ever had friend more staunch than the stocky, heavy-set man of middle age who now returned steadily Tumu-nui's gaze. He was constructed, not for beauty, but for solidity. Everything about Hoa Pahi ran to generous width. From the feet which gripped the earth so firmly, up the short tattooed legs to the massive trunk and shoulders all was wide, wide. It was true even of the face: a nose flattened at the base; a mouth which spread far from side to side, squarish at the corners and filled with strong white teeth; eyebrows thick and bushy, meeting in the middle to form a solid black line below his broad, receding forehead. Handsome?—no. *Serviceable* was the word, as many a thrown wrestler could have testified. Rata loved him.

"Yes, Tumu-nui." Hoa Pahi's voice was pitched to the deep roll of a temple drum. "We wait only for you before the priests carry the idol to the ship's marae. Then we may heave up the anchors."

"Good," the king replied. "We will go aboard." He went to the inner wall of the house and there, one by one, took down his weapons.

For a moment Hoa Pahi and Rata were left standing alone. Quickly, in an undertone, the older man asked, "What troubles you, youngster?"

"What indeed! I am left behind—I who stand inches taller than yourself."

"Yes," the helmsman chuckled, "and who weigh perhaps a half as much."

"Weight! What matters that?"

"A great deal, I can assure you, if Short-wave and Long-wave have a ship in their grip and you fight with the tiller."

"Yes, yes. I know. But I must go. I must go with you! Help me, Hoa Pahi."

The stolid mariner looked down at the carrying-bar and the greenish fruit which Rata had dropped to the sanded floor. Speculatively he rubbed his jutting, forethrust chin. "If you are so intent upon it," he observed at last, "I suppose you might somehow manage to turn yourself into a breadfruit. Of course there would be risk and perhaps some discomfort, but . . ."

Suddenly Rata laughed, and bending down he grasped the stout pole and swung it to his back. "Thank you, Hoa Pahi. I shall do as you say."

He darted from the house.

II

SLOWLY, RATA," he told himself when he was in the streets. "Walk slowly as does a man who looks forward to nothing more than laying down the carried burden. Let no one think your steps lead elsewhere than to a simple task's completion; let no one guess that already you have set foot upon a road of glory." But how hard was dissimulation when he felt like crying out in joy! Already, so it seemed, he trod a ship's lifting, falling, living decks. Surely this was not the tame old earth against which his toughened soles were pressing? Rata's thoughts had far outstripped his lagging body to gain the clean-swept, bounding seas.

He pressed through the massed rows of warriors who waited for their king, and many spoke to him as they made way. "Mea maitai?" they inquired, "You are well, king's son?"

On this wondrous morning there was something almost ludicrous in the simple greeting. Well? All his days had been passed in slumber and only now he'd come alive. Maitai? Oh, yes! he was well—and it was hard to suppress a burst of laughter. Yet he was cautious, made quiet answer. "Thanks, Teuru; soft thanks, Tutu." He looked at them intently, half fearing them to read his bold intention. Only when Timi gave a slap at the clusters of firm green spheres exclaiming jovially, "At least, Rata, we shall never die of hunger," did he come near to forgetting himself. "I shall also taste of these ship's stores!" he thought, and bit his tongue before the words escaped.

15

But at last the gauntlet of the crowded village was safely run. Walking a little faster now, he skirted the gathering of priests immobile at the water's edge and continued down the beach. Soon he had passed from sight and stood in a secluded cove where grew a single large fara tree. Drawn far up in its protecting shade was the small outrigger which he himself had made.

Although Rata had arrived at the threshold of manhood he was not yet done with the ways of youth, and a wide grin of satisfaction

spread across his face. He was a clever fellow and no one could hold so much as faint suspicion. The painful reserve dropped from him like cloaking tapa that is flung aside, and he rushed for his canoe. Feverishly he threw off the covering of dried coconut fronds, placed the breadfruit in the center, then, grasping the cross-beam, lifted high the bow and started for the sea. He took three steps, dragging the narrow hull after him—then halted, listening. Had someone spoken . . . ? He wheeled and scanned the beach to either side. It was deserted. But of course. No one would think to wander abroad when a fleet was about to sail. Again he bent his back and gripped the smooth-adzed beam.

"You, too, are going," a quiet voice said distinctly; and to Rata, now frankly startled, it seemed to issue from the limpid air above. Slowly he lowered the canoe and as slowly turned.

"Yes? Does the spirit of a departed ancestor speak to me?" he inquired a little unsteadily. Low laughter was the only reply and, seeking, he looked up into the fara tree.

"Turia!" he exclaimed, relieved yet annoyed. "It is only you!" The girl lay close against a bare, steeply sloping limb, her dark head nearly hidden by one of the pandanus leaf tufts which blossomed from each branch-tip. "Why are you here?" he demanded impatiently.

She slid down till her bare feet touched the ground; then, turning with her back to the gray, stilt-supported trunk, regarded him with eyes from which all trace of mirth was gone. "For what should I wait in the village?" she asked. "Tani went aboard at dawn; I have no one else to whom to say farewell."

Rata was fond of Turia's brother. Fond, yet, at the minute, more than a little envious. For though Turia was of an age with himself, Tani, who stood no taller, was two, perhaps three, years older and could sail with no thought to subterfuge. Years, however, were to make no difference! He cast a hasty glance to his canoe, a glance which the girl interpreted with ease.

"You are both the same," she stated solemnly. Her arms were at her sides, the palms of her slender hands pressing lightly the bark of the tree, her eyes holding his with their level unquestioning gaze. "You both believe the seas to be a playground made alone for your pleasure, for excitement and adventure. You are so young!"

"And you are equally so, Turia," he said shortly, "although you make sounds like an old woman."

"Yet I have lived long enough to remember more than one fine ship that has sailed—and not returned."

"They will return," he asserted firmly.

" 'They'?—or 'we'?"

He looked at the tall girl with something approaching anger. "What makes you think I also am leaving?"

"I know," she told him with a slow smile.

THE SHIP OF FLAME

Rata's brows rose slightly but not precisely in surprise. He was long since past surprise where Turia was concerned. That she had the ability to guess his inmost thoughts he had discovered months ago when first she came from her chieftain father's lands on Tahiti's lee-ward shores. Sent by her parents to learn the ways of the court and capital, she had lived, as her high birth entitled her to do, beneath the same royal roof which had always sheltered Rata himself. He had noticed that in her expressive eyes shadows swam like passing clouds that momentarily film the transparent deeps of a lagoon. Formerly it had been only curious and amusing that they saw so much more than others; now, suddenly, it was become a hazard standing between him and his most desired goal.

"Turia," he said earnestly, "will you not put your lips together and hold them closed?"

Briefly her eyelids lowered and she nodded. "Yes."

"Tightly? Tightly as the lips of a frightened clam?"

Again he saw the effortless, and somehow disturbing, smile. "Are you not stronger than my Tani," she asked, "stronger than many of the crew? Why should you not sail?"

Rata drew himself to his full height. Why not, indeed? Turia spoke a truth and it was a pleasant truth to hear. How could he have been angry? She was very sensible. More than sensible, really. . . . He had taken a step toward her when he caught himself. Of what was he thinking? Time was short! With a bound he was again beside his canoe, wrenching it from the wetly sucking sands, launching it upon the waters of the bay, swinging vigorously the carven paddle. Assured of her silence, he put Turia from his mind.

But though she would say nothing of Rata's plans, Turia's lips were not such as may tightly close. They remained half parted in a pensive smile as she watched him hurriedly propelling his little craft out to the busy lanes where many small dugouts plied between three anchored ships and shore. There, last-minute supplies were being stowed aboard and there, too, last-minute embraces were being exchanged between sailors and loved ones left behind. Her brother, still dazzled by his own good fortune to be part of the king's fleet on a voyage to distant lands, had left with hardly a word—Rata without a single one.

Turia lifted up her face, the mass of her night-black waist-long hair cascading down her back, and gave a vigorous shake of her head so that, like dark mist, the soft mane spread lightly about her shoulders. It was a gesture of Tahitian women which is old as time and may have had no other meaning than the freeing of tangled locks. But it may also be that it was Turia's way of quietly accepting the unavoidable. Tani and Rata—they were both the same. Could one make them otherwise?

She turned and walked away from the sea.

III

HE was abreast of the flagship when a loud cheering rose up from the shore and Rata knew that his father and Queen Maemae had appeared and, flanked by armed warriors on either side, were making their way through the village. For a moment the attention of all on the ship was centered shoreward. The crew had gathered in the bows to witness the approach of the king and the barge carrying the protecting image of Oro, god of war.

Coming up to the stern of the big ship, Rata flung the strings of breadfruit to the deck above and leaped aboard. Quickly, then, he shouldered his burden once more and ran below. The hulls of the war canoe were divided into various compartments, some containing sails and lines and gear, some filled with spears, stone axes, knives and missiles. In still others, live pigs and fowls were tethered. Just below the platform on which Hoa Pahi always stood to guide the ship was a hold stored almost to the planking overhead with drinking nuts, taro root and breadfruit. Here Rata threw down his load. The chant of priests with punctuating, solemn drumbeat had begun again, and the barge would already be on its way across the water. In the dim light he set rapidly to work. To right and left he threw the heavy clusters of drinking nuts, the unwieldy bunches of taro, the rough-skinned breadfruit. Twice he stopped to listen, fearing the commotion must have been heard, but no footsteps approached and again he attacked the mountain of food. When he had dug a hollow sufficiently large he seated himself within and pulled the piled stores down from all sides till the weight upon his chest was such that he could hardly breathe, till nothing protruded from the massed vegetables but his own head. He had, at Hoa Pahi's suggestion, become a breadfruit. If no one brought a light below before they were out to sea he was safe, for, once beyond the pass, his father would not put about. To do so would be to invite disaster on the voyage ahead; the gods show no favor to those who hesitate, turn back.

Drums and voices of singers became loud. There was grating of wood on wood as the heavy barge of Oro came alongside, and the deck resounded with the tread of running feet. It may not have been a great while before the idol was safely installed beneath the thatch roof of the marae forward, with banana shoots spread out on the altar at its feet. But to Rata, waiting in the half darkness, it seemed long and he sighed with relief when the rattling of the matting sail against the mast told him that the double canoe of Tumu-nui was under way. Almost simultaneously a great shout went up from the people of Tahiti who stood close-packed along the shore. It was answered by the hundred warriors aboard the ship in which Rata rode and by those on the two accompanying vessels. Then the long paddles dipped into the sea, hurrying the canoes beyond the lee of the land where the full strength of the trade wind would bear them away.

Rata knew that all depended on the next few minutes. The pass to the outer ocean lay a bare half mile from shore and he was tempted to throw off the weight which pressed upon him and to rush on deck for a last look at the palm-studded coast of his homeland. He tried to picture to himself the receding shore. Already a quarter of the distance to the reef must have been covered, perhaps a third. Was it earlier on this same morning that he had passed through the familiar village streets thinking only of leaving them behind, thinking them humdrum and unexciting, close to scorning the very earth which supported him? Ah, to walk thus upon fair Tahiti was mistake, was blindness, as one learned the moment he was gone. To venture forth was very fine, but it had taken Rata little time to guess the happiness of safe return. He found himself recalling the faces of those who had remained, those of friends, of kin, of his uncle Iore, of Queen Maemae. For minutes the thought of Queen Maemae lingered in his mind; then, with a slight start, he realized that Turia had taken her place. Her voice came back to him. "More than one fine ship has sailed—and not returned." There was something vaguely disquieting in her words as there was in the girl herself. He brushed them aside. Lesser vessels might come to grief, might fail to raise again the splendid peak called Orofena, but not his father's flagship.

Suddenly Rata's body became rigid: there was a scraping on the ladder rungs as someone descended to the hold. So soon? For what reason? But reasons were plentiful. The man might be seeking sennit line and hook of shell to run out for fish; he might be off watch and merely going forward to the crew's quarters to find his mat and stretch himself upon it. Or he might be thirsty, which would bring him directly to the hold in which Rata lay surrounded by enough food to last the expedition forty days and by countless drinking nuts to quench their thirst for an equal time. Might the gods forbid the man to seek food or drink! The footsteps came nearer. They came on till the faintly outlined frame of the doorway was filled with the bulk of a turbaned warrior. The fellow was muttering under his breath, and he stooped to paw about among the piles of produce. Rata did not stop to think that the man, fresh from the glare of the outside sun, could hardly see his hand before his face; he thought only of his own head, which he imagined to protrude conspicuously as does a swimming turtle's above a quiet lagoon. With a convulsive wriggle he tried to burrow farther down, and in so doing set in motion a rumbling avalanche which rolled thumping down about the startled intruder. When it was over, Rata was left completely exposed from head to foot.

"On deck!" the man shouted at the top of his lungs. "Pigs have gotten to the stores!" and he lunged forward to grasp what he mistakenly believed to be a surprisingly agile boar.

Rata wrenched himself free and sprang to his feet. His hand found a heavy bunch of taro roots which were bound tight together. He swung them high and brought them down upon his adversary. But it was not enough; Tahitian skulls are thick. The cries for help did not cease, although it now appeared the other had gathered it was not pigs with which he had to deal.

"On deck!" he continued to shout. "On deck! Men with silent paddles have boarded us in the night!"

THE SHIP OF FLAME

If more were needed to make the alarm general it was thus supplied, for in those days Tahiti was subject to frequent raids by the people of Eimeo and Tahaa and especially Vavau.* Those of the latter island had surprised King Tumu-nui and his warriors more than once by approaching in darkness with muffled paddles, and now the conviction quickly seized all aboard that the crafty men of Vavau had stowed away and were about to storm the ship. Although Rata was locked with his assailant in a struggle which sent them both careening against the bulkheads of the narrow storeroom, he could hear clearly the angry cries which rose above.

"Death to the Papaas †—death to the foreigners! Death to the tricksters of Vavau!" Men armed with spears and hatchets plummeted down the hatchways and darted this way and that in the bowels of the ship searching for the horde of invaders. Several forced their way in where Rata fought and would soon have struck his head from his body if he had not had the presence of mind to see that further resistance was useless.

"It is Rata!" he gasped. "The son of Tumu-nui."

The others stopped with weapons raised. Was it possible? The Prince of Tahiti hidden here in the bottom of the ship? They took him with them, leading him upwards to the light, and exclamations of surprise came from the lips of the men they passed. "Rata, son of the king! What does he here?" He was brought aft to the platform where Hoa Pahi with King Tumu-nui beside him leaned his muscular, sun-blackened back against the great steering paddle. The sail had been lowered, as had those of the other vessels, and all three drifted very nearly in the center of the pass.

Tumu-nui bent a stern glance upon his son. Disheveled though he was, Rata seemed unabashed and it was clear that in his opinion it was no crime to want to be a man and join in man's adventures. The king turned and looked into the homely face of his steersman, who appeared to be studying the erratic flight of a pair of terns about the masthead. "Hoa Pahi," said he, "how has this come about? Did you not make your usual inspection of the ship?"

"Yes," the other replied without lowering his gaze.

* Now known as Bora Bora.
† Spelled *popaa* in modern Tahitian, the word has come to mean "white man."

22

"And did you discover nothing?"

Hoa Pahi scratched one of his large, protruding ears. He shifted his weight from one stocky leg to the other. "I saw many hundred bread-fruit, Tumu-nui, but if your son has the power to become one with them it is no wonder that I was not the wiser."

The king's features relaxed somewhat and it may be that he was not unable to remember the days when he was himself of Rata's age, and to recall how strong would have been his own desire to share the dangers of distant seas. But to Hoa Pahi he said, "I suspect that you know more of this than you care to admit."

Hoa Pahi's eyes now lowered so that they met the king's; they were wide so that the whites seemed very prominent and they held an expression of exaggerated innocence. "Have I ever failed to serve you faithfully?" he demanded.

"No," the other conceded, "with one exception I believe you would put no man before me."

"With one exception!" the helmsman exclaimed, genuinely startled. "And who is that?"

A faint smile touched Tumu-nui's lips. "My son," he said simply. Then, turning to the youth, "You have done a serious thing, Rata. You have brought the fleet to a stop when it was nearly at large and you have disobeyed me by leaving your mother's side, which is your rightful place in my absence. Yet we cannot turn back; even to rest thus with lowered sails at the outset of our voyage is to risk the displeasure of the gods."

Caught in the strong out-bound current, the three vessels were moving swiftly through the pass, and King Tumu-nui's eyes were troubled as he scanned the half-mile expanse of water which lay now between them and the dwindling village. People on shore who had started to leave were returning to watch anxiously the drifting war canoes.

"I cannot," Rata's father continued, "command you to go, for it is a long and difficult swim worthy of any warrior, while you are not yet full grown."

Rata stiffened. "If I am not yet grown, father," he said with considerable truth, "then surely shall I become the greatest man in all Tahiti. And as for swimming home, I have no fear. Yet it would be easier to cover twice the distance if it were to join you."

"That is well said," the king replied, and a note of tenderness crept into his voice. "I almost believe you could do so. But each of us has a duty to perform. We must not turn from it." Suddenly his customary reserve left him and he stretched forth his hands. "Come, let me embrace you a last time!"

Rata rushed to him and was locked in his father's arms. Tumu-nui held his son tightly—so tightly that the pendant boar's tusks which adorned his broad chest bit into the youth's flesh. And it was in this minute that it came to Rata with full force that this was indeed a parting. Till now he had held to the vain hope that perhaps the expedition would not leave or that, somehow, if it did he would go as well. This was not the first time that father and son would be separated, for King Tumu-nui made frequent journeys to Eimeo and Huahine, but these islands were but few miles distant and only a week or two passed before lookouts posted in the tallest coconut trees cried out the return of the canoes. How different this was to be! Not weeks but agonizing months would pass before the fleet could be expected.

At last the pressure of Tumu-nui's arms relaxed and Rata drew away. There was silence while the men rested on their paddles with eyes averted from their king and prince. Only Hoa Pahi looked directly at the two, and Rata saw his thick lips form a single word: courage! He forced a smile for the big helmsman, a smile which told him again, "Thank you, Friend-of-the-Ship." Aloud he said, "Hoa Pahi, guide my father back to me." Then, without trusting himself for another glance at his father's face, he dove from the war canoe and plunged into the sea. When his head came to the surface he struck out, still without looking back, against the swiftly flowing current. He heard the shouts of the sailors as they hoisted sail; he heard the scores of paddles dipping rhythmically. Then, quickly, the sounds grew faint as the fleet rushed out to the open sea.

It was not till he had almost reached the shore that Rata allowed himself to turn. The sun was lowering toward the fantastic, jutting peaks of Eimeo and the entire horizon was rimmed with clouds which towered up in slowly changing monster-shapes, causing the three vessels to look pitifully frail. Toy boats they had become—toy boats such as children make of a dried leaf—their human cargo dwarfed and small. Yet on the raised stern of the flagship two figures still were clear. One was broad and short, the other tall. Tumu-nui stood grave and commanding with his eyes on the tossing desert of waves which stretched ahead.

So Rata remembered him. Always.

IV

MANY MOONS passed over the mountains of Tahiti to slide down into the sea behind the sister island of Eimeo. Still the fleet of King Tumu-nui did not return and no word of him came from the silent ocean. A feeling of gloom and of disquiet had begun to take hold of all the people. Had Tumu-nui, the unconquerable in war, met his equal in some far-off land? Had unnamable disaster overtaken the proud flotilla so that the bones of all the brave warriors now lay strewn on the dark ocean floor? Rumors spread from mouth to mouth; soothsayers and sorcerers made their brews and cast their spells. From week to week the unrest and despondency grew.

"He will return," Rata still insisted staunchly when the wild tales of ruin reached his ears. "Has my father ever failed in what he undertook?" Yet questionings and gnawing doubts entered his own mind as well in spite of all his faith. Surely Hoa Pahi would find his way? Surely he would steer his father back to harbor's safety?

It was the season of rains. For days on end the sun was hidden behind heavy banks of clouds, clouds which drenched the village in sodden downpour. Swirling mist and rain filled the valleys and wrapped the mountains in a dense gray shroud. An angry swell had set in upon the leaden sea and hammered heavily with mournful, deep-toned booming upon the coral barrier.

Four persons were gathered beneath the roof of Tumu-nui's oval palace of thatch and sweet bamboo. Although it was midmorning, a string of candlenuts, planted in the center of the white sand floor, burned ruddily. In a circle about the little flame several mats were spread. Upon one of them Queen Maemae and Turia were seated, their hands deftly turning the leaf baskets which they wove. On another lay Iore, who stared into space unseeingly. Lastly there was Rata, squatting on his heels, holding a stout length of purau wood over which he vigorously rubbed the rough hide of a shark. Already the beautifully grained wood had taken on a high polish.

Iore shifted his gaunt frame to a more comfortable position and bent sad eyes upon his nephew. "If that is to be a bow, Rata, there is no man living strong enough to bend it."

Rata ceased his work and turned to the man who held the place of his absent father. "Do you still continue, uncle, to consider me a boy?" he inquired smiling.

"You are little more. Why do you ask?"

"Because in that case," Rata replied, back at his polishing, "what you say may very well be true. Unless it be my father, no man lives who might draw it; yet I shall do so."

Iore rose irritably "If it were not amusing such conceit would be little short of insufferable!"

Rata glanced up in mild astonishment at his uncle's vehemence, but the older man left the house without further speech. "Is there cause for anger? I have said no more than . . ."

"You have said what you believe, Rata," Turia told him simply. "It is what your mother and I believe as well. But you must not be surprised that tempers are short—short with long waiting."

He regarded her gratefully. Turia's words were never many but invariably they fell pleasantly on the ear. She was, he thought, very unlike other women. He recalled the endless wagging of tongues which his unsuccessful attempt to stow away had caused. Some there had been who condemned Rata's rashness on that occasion; yet most, in their hearts, were proud of his ambition. Nevertheless, the gossip, the chatter and speculation had filled him with distaste. Turia, who had shared his secret and well knew his bitter disappointment, met him when he was coming from the beach with sea water streaming from his limbs. "There will be another sailing," she had said; and nothing more. "Yes," he'd replied, still breathless from the long swim, "another sailing," and they had gone on to the house together.

Rata smiled. "Iore makes the sound of a man who has eaten shark."

Queen Maemae's fingers moved nimbly over the basket she was weaving. "You should try not to annoy your uncle," she said gently. Then, after a pause, " He is greatly troubled; troubled even as I."

Something in his mother's tone caused Rata to put his bow aside. She, like Turia, was dressed most simply on that day. Her only garment was a brown pareu on which was worked an angular design in black and white. It was such a pareu as might have been worn by the humblest of her subjects and was wrapped about her body—a body nearly as slender as Turia's own—so that it covered her breasts and reached no farther than the knees. Her luxuriant hair fell softly forward, shading her lovely face. Only recently, it seemed to him, had he begun to realize Turia's disturbing charm, but that his mother was beautiful he thought he had always known. Never before, however, had the awareness been so keen, and now in some strange way it brought him pain. He felt he could not bear that she should feel hurt or sorrow; the gods might bring loss and suffering to others, but not to her! There must be some way to cheer, some way to hearten and encourage. If the rain would stop, if the dark clouds would go away; if only the sun would shine . . .

He was about to speak when a sound cut him short. It was faint and still far off. In the distance it had a chillingly human note but Rata knew it instantly. The cry of the bird of paradise. "Oti'i!" it called, "Oti'i!" The fingers of both women had stopped their busy weaving and they listened with still lowered heads.

"No nearer!" Rata prayed silently. "Come no nearer, bird of evil tidings!" Those in the house of the king sat motionless, waiting—wait-

27

ing for the cry of a long-tailed bird with gaudy plumage gold and white. A minute passed. Other sounds were suddenly, queerly loud and plain: the swish of rain on sodden ground, the rattling fall of a dead and withering coco frond, the choked wail of an infant in a near-by dwelling, the grinding of seas against the solid reef.

"Oti'i! Oti'i!" It came from directly over their heads; the bird might have been hovering above the very ridgepole.

"Repeat!" Turia exclaimed quickly. "Bird of paradise, speak once again!" And they waited, more tensely than before. Even children could have told the meaning and the reason of Turia's words, for who does not know that if the brilliant fowl is heard within a dwelling it must give voice a second time when bidden, that if it fail to do so death has come among the family concerned?

Rata sat with his head tilted back, staring upward at the neatly overlapping strips of pandanus which formed the roof. He stared as if he would see through the softly mottled covering of leaves into the limitless outside air, into the wet sky where a bird dipped and soared—but silently. More minutes slipped by. Once he thought he heard the beat of wings, but even of this he was not sure. Then he realized that both Turia and his mother had resumed their work.

"Mother! Turia! Look at me."

Turia had turned away, but after a moment's hesitation Queen Maemae raised her head. "What is it, Rata?"

He gazed long into her eyes and she made no move to avert them, unable or, perhaps, unwilling to disguise what lay there clear to be seen. Quickly, impulsively, he rose and went to her, seated himself close beside and placed a hand over the slender, nimbly moving fingers so that they were stilled.

"You are afraid, little mother. You are both afraid."

She smiled very faintly. "Yes, Rata, we are."

"Perhaps the bird answered. Perhaps his call was carried away by the wind and rain; perhaps . . ." He fell silent, not believing his own words, sensing their empty sound.

Yet his mother said, "It may be so. But in any case our fear is not of the bird of paradise. Whether he speaks or flies mute can in no way change our lives and fortunes. It is not he who guides our destinies, and he tells us, if anything at all, only of what the gods have brought to pass, which no man may change." She looked at her son intently.

"You are surprised, I think, to discover that even a Queen of Tahiti may be afraid. Perhaps this knowledge comes as a shock to you but you must understand that your parents, rulers though they be, are simple mortals. And there is much in the world that is mysterious, dark and unknowable. You must not wonder, then, if I tell you that ever since your father and his followers sailed away the fear for them has dwelt within me. Tumu-nui is brave and generous and kind of heart. Yet, like Turia's brother, he is but a man and we are all exceeding small on the face of the earth, small beside the mountains which rise at our backs, small beside the waves which leap from the ocean's breast. And what is our strength compared to the gods of winds and storms, compared to thunder and lightnings or to the living monsters which swim the salt blue seas and the spirits which fly by the night air? We are very ignorant, even those of us who are thought great, and it sometimes seems to me that we exist only at the merest whim of these forces, overwhelming strong, which crowd us on all sides."

Never before had Rata known his mother to speak to him in this way. He was reminded of times he had overheard her talking to his father, times when neither King Tumu-nui nor his queen had been aware of any listener. At first her manner had perplexed him. Then, with quiet pride, he realized that she spoke to him as an equal. Nor was he less quick to appreciate that it was because his mother needed him, needed his resilient youth to lean upon in her husband's absence, needed the love and companionship of a son.

He pressed her hand firmly. "Let us take courage, beloved. All you say may be very true. Yet I, too, am strong. Have you not remarked," he inquired, "how I have grown in these last months?"

At his words Turia raised her head and Rata saw tears glisten in her eyes, but he saw also the smile that touched her mouth.

Queen Maemae nodded her head. Indeed she had noticed her son's growth. She had watched it, even with some alarm, and had recalled more than once his fervent wish: May I grow to twice the size of other men! Often she had remembered, too, the sudden flight of the man-of-war bird through the quiet air of the house. That Oro himself had heard she had no longer doubt. "Yes, Rata," she replied, "I have seen you pass the height of your uncle Iore, and today, if your father stood beside you, I believe you would be of even measure. And yet your years are so few in number!"

29

He sprang to his feet. "Then shall I have many more in which to protect and care for you." He paused, his expression sobered. "It is good also," he added slowly, "that years stretch before me in which to avenge my father's death if he is truly lost to us."

"Not yet, Rata. Do not think of vengeance while we still wait in darkness knowing nothing. We must not cease to hope. And, above all, we must not betray our fears. The people need badly our support and we must devise means of taking their minds from the trouble that besets us." The queen's eyes rested on Rata's nearly completed bow.

"What do you think, Turia," she asked, "should we not call a meet for the archers so that all may watch the contest?"

"Ah, yes!" Rata exclaimed, whipping up the weapon from the floor. "My bow shall compete with the others. Would you know its name? It is called Star-that-flies-by-night!" His mother was smiling up at him and he stopped short, overcome to think that their sorrow and his had so quickly gone from mind.

"You must not reproach yourself," she said, noting his sudden change of expression. "No men were ever better loved than those who sailed away. But it is not fitting that our thoughts dwell on them to the exclusion of all else. They would not have it so. We have our own lives to live, and whether we are again to see Tani's or King Tumu-nui's face is not for us to say." Rata's mother looked through the open doorway, over which the eaves hung protectingly low. A short time before the rain had run in steady rivulets from each brown pandanus leaf; now it dripped but slowly. A little of the gloom which had so long overspread the village appeared to have dispersed. The sky was clearing.

"I believe," said the queen, "we shall see the sun by afternoon. Go, then, to your uncle and tell him it is my wish the archers prepare themselves. If the thought of fleeting arrows can give my son a moment's forgetfulness of care it should do far more for the people at large."

Rata tightened the maro about his loins and started out. The two women watched him as he went, watched his long, confident strides and the easy swing of his bared shoulders, watched as he lowered his head to pass beneath the arched tamanu which formed the entrance to the king's house.

"So tall," Queen Maemae whispered. "Like Tumu-nui, so tall, so poised and strong." Bending forward she picked up the uncompleted basket in her hands.

But Turia's eyes remained on the doorway through which he had passed.

V

BY MIDAFTERNOON the sun bathed all Tumu-nui's kingdom in its brilliant light. The fronds of coco palms and bananas, the big round leaves of purau trees, the pointed blades of bamboo and the heavy, pendulous elephant ear— all were a clean, bright green. The air, too, seemed washed and clear, so clear that one could see far into the deepest jungle-filled valleys, far onto the mountains where cascades still raced frothing white over the slopes. Here and there high clouds, torn and wispy, hurried down the sky toward the Many-Islands which lie out of sight below the horizon. The sea had lost its sullen look and was a white-flecked blue. Waves continued to foam over the reefs, but boobies and terns and other sea birds had already alighted on the water, a sign that increasing calm was to be expected.

In the village, however, there was growing movement as people from near-by settlements swelled the throng in the lanes between the houses. They came from the north, following the beach at the foot of the cliff from which Rata had looked down on his father's fleet, and they came from the south over the trail which wound inland through green fields and over low hills, yet never far from the sea. They came also by canoe, following the well-known channels of the lagoon. All converged on King Tumu-nui's capital, the women carrying babes in their arms, the men with spears and those of noble families with their bows and quivers, for the messengers sent by Iore had spread the word that those archers still remaining in the land should assemble to try their skill.

Faces looked brighter than they had for many long weeks, and shouted greetings were exchanged between canoe and canoe and between group and group on the grassy streets. What was more fitting, they asked each other, than a meet for the archers? Queen Maemae had shown herself both shrewd and wise, for such a contest held something of the nature of a religious ceremony, a ceremony which might well hurry their beloved king's return. Never was bow and arrow used in war. What man would be so cowardly as to attack another from a distance or deal a blow if his own bared chest were not there to receive another in return? None of the island called Tahiti. The flight of slender bamboo arrows was a thing of beauty and pleasing to the gods; never, therefore, was the bow put to other use.

Queen Maemae and Turia had left with their attendants for the open glade where they would take places in the center of the spectators beneath a shading mango, and Rata was alone in his father's house. Clad in the white tapa girdle of archers and the royal belt of ura feathers, he bent over his mighty bow. With practiced fingers he made fast the stout hempen cord to either end, then straightened and held the weapon at arm's length. A smile played over his lips. "Star-that-flies-by-night," he murmured, "serve me well this day." Yet as he continued to survey the tough length of purau in his hands the smile slowly faded. Would he, perhaps, be wiser to test the bow before entering the games? Impossible that he should fail to bend the six-foot arc. Unthinkable. Unthinkable that a king's son should suffer ridicule. He hesitated, looking at the filled quiver at his feet, then, stooping, whipped an arrow from the long yellow cylinder of bamboo and fitted it to the string. With a knee to the ground he sighted along the shaft to the sharp-whittled point which must be drawn back till it met fingers locked about the bow at its thickest. Rata took a breath. Slowly his body stiffened, stiffened till the muscles of back and arms tensed, stood out clear and hard. Did Iore say no man alive could draw this shining weapon? The smile, now grim, had reappeared and the hand which gripped the string began to move. Back, back it came, inch by inch while the arc of the bow and the strain increased. "Come, Night-Star," Rata's lips formed the words silently, "bend to the strength of my right arm!" There was a crackling in the polished wood and the weapon trembled in his grasp. But his hand came to a halt a foot from his right ear and the head of the arrow still protruded a foot from the center of the bow. To stop here was failure. But a king's son *cannot* fail—not Tumu-nui's son! Perspiration started out on his brow and a sudden dizziness attacked him. The arrow moved no farther. With a rush the air came from his lungs and at the same time his muscles relaxed. He lowered the bow till it rested on the ground before him and for some moments remained there with still labored breath, shaking his head slowly from side to side. Had he, after all, fashioned a bow which no mortal man should ever use? With a twinge of pain he recalled his mother's and Turia's quiet faith.

Suddenly he imagined he could hear mocking laughter, taunting, jesting voices.

"This Rata must think himself superior to ordinary men. Since when has he taken on such airs?" There was more laughter and then again the same voice: "Where is this astounding bow of which we hear? And where is the dauntless archer?"

Rata got quickly to his feet. He knew that voice and he knew the loud laugh which followed it. These were no echoings of his imagination but blatant sounds which came from the throat of Teo-teo of Pare village, the vain and over-proud winner of the last archers' meet.

Teo-teo and the group of young men with whom he walked came on till they stood just without. "Oh, Rata!" came the scoffing voice.

"Come forth with your giant's bow that we may wonder and admire. Let us see this weapon which will wing your arrows to the sun."

The blood mounted to Rata's face, suffusing the brown skin with a darker tint. His grasp tightened about the bow and he half raised it from the ground. If it was never to serve him on the archers' field then might it well do for a club to shorten abruptly that maddening laughter. He took an impulsive step toward the door—but then he halted. He looked down at the bow in his hands. With what care he had shaped, polished, whittled and polished again. With what pleasure he had watched it take form from the rough branch. Was there ever an instrument more graceful, more suggestive of inherent, tight-leashed power, more fitting to games for the pleasure of gods? And what had he been about to do—use Star-that-flies-by-night as a common stave with which to fight a brawl? Oro forbid that he ever so completely lose his senses!

He snatched up the quiver, bound it about his waist by the sennit belt, slipped the bow over his shoulder and stepped to the door. "Look your fill, Teo-teo," he said. "Here is the weapon you speak of and here also is the man who wields it."

Teo-teo fell back and his mouth opened, but some time passed before a sound came from it. He had last seen Rata on the day when the three war canoes made sail. Months had since passed, to be sure, but he was momentarily bewildered by the change which had taken place in King Tumu-nui's son. The man from Pare remembered a gangling, big-eyed youngster, yet now he faced a youth taller than himself, taller, he judged, than almost any man of Tahiti; and a youth, furthermore, whose calm and stern expression had a strangely sobering effect upon the recently hooting and jeering company.

Teo-teo looked dubiously at the great bow resting across Rata's back. It is true, he thought, this young fellow has sprouted like a banana shoot in fertile soil; but surely that weapon is too much for him. They say he has never been seen to use it. Is this, then, the day of trial? He decided that it must be so, and his good spirits returned to him. Rata would surely fail and of all the competitors he would himself once more send an arrow to the greatest distance. These considerations warmed him and filled him with such pleasure that he put a patronizing arm about Rata.

"Come, Prince," said he. "One glance at your bow convinces me that today I must step down in defeat, but I am a generous man and hold no ill feeling."

His companions again laughed appreciatively at their leader's sarcasm, although now with a trace of uneasiness, and only Rata was silent. Yet he fell into step as they set out for the field where most of the people had assembled. The path was of such width that two could walk abreast, and Rata walked ahead with Teo-teo while the others followed.

Tall flowering lilies and hibiscus grew on either side, and as the two youths entered the mouth of the valley a quantity of birds were to be seen on the green slopes. They flitted back and forth among the mango and mape and breadfruit trees, filling the air with their shrill cries. Wild pigeons of a green still brighter than the foliage, swallows of shining black, thrushes with wings of lightest yellow mingled with countless varieties of parakeets—parakeets solid purple, the birds of royalty; red and yellow, the symbols of Oro; black with white breasts, the shadows of mountain elves; blue and green, the spirits of goddesses of the air. But Rata, usually so filled with delight by the myriad birds which crowded his island, Rata who had often climbed the steep mountain sides to watch the wild red-feathered ducks which inhabited the lake cupped by an old volcano, Rata who had paddled stealthily the lagoons to spy on the brown heron or the nesting gulls or the snow-white sea swallows, now walked with unseeing eyes fixed straight before him, unaware of the fresh beauty of the rain-washed valley or of the birds which swooped down close to his bared head. What awaited him at the end of this pleasant winding path? Disgrace? Now, for the first time since his father's departure, he was glad King Tumu-nui was away. At least his father would not see the sorry spectacle nor hear the cries of scorn. Rata's ears burned even as he thought of it, for, though there was at that time no living soul on the island of Tahiti with better courage, there is, of course, nothing harder to bear than ridicule. In Tumu-nui's kingdom a man built his bow to suit his strength; its size and toughness announced to his fellows the estimate he placed upon himself. "This," it said in effect, "is what I think of my own ability." None but a boaster proclaims himself better than he is; none but a braggart appears upon the field with a weapon he cannot master.

The path came to an end and the young men stepped forth into the glade of archers.

VI

THE walls of the valley here fell away on either side to narrow and converge once more a quarter mile farther inland, thus enclosing a plain of roughly circular shape, bare of trees, and covered with ankle-high grass which waved gently in a light breeze from sea. Reclining in the shade of a grove of ancient trees, and flanked on either side by the massed spectators, were Queen Maemae and her court.

The newcomers marched across the green to receive from her the flower admitting them to the games. Teo-teo's chest expanded as he took the small white gardenia from her hand, placed it behind his left ear, and swaggered off. When Rata, in his turn, took the outstretched blossom from his mother, it was with averted eyes. He tried to leave quickly, but with a soft word she detained him.

"Remember, my son," said she, speaking so quietly that her voice reached no others, "remember the reason for these games; nothing else is of importance."

He knew her meaning well. Everywhere he looked he saw happy, eager, expectant faces. The minds of the people, temporarily at least, were indeed taken from the sorrow which beset them. But she did not understand! There were other things of importance. A king's son *must* not fail. He raised his head to find Turia's direct gaze full upon him. When he had started back onto the field her confident words came to him: "The bow will bend; you shall see."

The blast of a conch shell rang through the valley and the first of the archers took position. Far inland, attendants stood with flag-tipped poles to mark the fall of arrows. A cry went up from the crowd and the first flight of bamboo shafts sailed out over the sward from the raised platform at the seaward end of the clearing. The stage for bowmen was a triangle some four feet high built of heavy coral blocks, the base facing inland, and of a size sufficient to allow three men to kneel at once. Rata stood close beside it watching silently as three by three the archers stepped up to let fly their missiles. His turn, he knew, was far to come, for those of lesser rank were obliged to shoot first. But though there were long minutes still to wait before he must stand alone upon the platform, his hand clenched unconsciously about his bow, and the muscles in his right arm hardened as the memory of the unsuccessful trial continued to plague his mind.

Teo-teo, lolling at ease and disdaining so much as a glance for the efforts of the others, turned to him. "What do you think—is this valley long enough to hold your bolt?" Then, noticing the moisture on the youth's brow, "You are nervous, Rata. Do you fear the weapon in your hands? If so you have reason, for, by the gods, it looks as though made for Oro himself."

"In that case," said Rata quietly, "may Oro lend me of his strength."

Teo-teo had ready a bantering reply, but a great shout from the crowd cut him short. He looked out onto the field. There, far away, stood a tall pole firmly implanted in the ground with a red flag waving at its tip. Teo-teo had long looked with satisfaction on that red flag; it stood on the spot where his own winning arrow had fallen some months before. But what was this? One of the attendants was racing toward it, was almost upon it . . . had passed it and still went on! At last, amid the wild cheering of the people, he came to a stop full ten yards beyond Teo-teo's record. With a flourish he drove in a new marker. Of a sudden the careless and indifferent pose of the former champion deserted him. An expression of dismayed astonishment came over his face, and he craned his neck to see above the heads of those surrounding him, craned his neck to see who had done this impossible thing. A stranger of medium height was quietly stepping down from the triangular platform. He moved calmly, deliberately, and his features betrayed no excitement. A wave of questions swept the populace. Who is this man? How is he called? From where does he come?

"Who has admitted him to the lists?" Teo-teo demanded loudly. "See—he does not wear the flower of the Queen!"

It was true. No gardenia rested behind his ear and it was clear he had entered the games without authority, a serious crime in Tahiti, where such competitions were reserved for those of noble birth alone. A clamor of protest rose on all sides, but again Teo-teo's voice was the loudest. "Remove the white flag!" he shouted. "Rule him out!"

Rata had remained motionless up to this time but now he came forward and placed a restraining hand on Teo-teo's arm. "Enough!" he said. "Be quiet, all of you. Let the man speak."

The stranger approached the group of archers unhurriedly. He came to a halt before Rata, and his somber eyes rested momentarily on the belt of crimson feathers which the young man wore over his bleached white loin cloth. Then he spoke in a tone which, although respectful, was in no way submissive. "Prince, I am a son of the Queen of Huahine. Tavae is my name. Do you begrudge a man from another land entry to your games?"

"We bar no nobleman," Rata replied, "yet since these contests are for the pleasure, not only of the people, but of the gods as well, they are tapu and governed by the strictest rules."

"That I well believe, and if I have broken the customs of this island I must plead the ignorance of a foreigner. We, too, have our tapus, but perhaps they are not in all respects the same as yours."

"You speak well, Tavae of Huahine. Even as well as you shoot. If my father, King Tumu-nui, were here he would not exclude a man with so skilled a tongue and bow." Rata took from behind his ear the gardenia given him by his mother and extended it to the stranger. "In his stead I welcome you."

Applause greeted Rata's declaration, and the next team of archers leaped upon the coral blocks. Only Teo-teo was silent, and, glancing at him, Rata saw that it was now his forehead which was damp with perspiration, his hand which clutched convulsively the handle of a bow.

If interest had been intense before, it was now doubled, for the contest was no longer a simple one between the villages of Tahiti but a struggle between two island kingdoms. Was a single man from Huahine to bring defeat upon all Tumu-nui's archers who still remained on land? Flight after flight of arrows swept inland toward the two distant flags, the one red and the other, still farther off, a challenging white. Groans of dismay escaped the people as one after another the bamboo shafts fell to earth short of the new record, short even of Teo-teo's best effort. A restless impatience seized the onlookers. "Bring on our champion!" they called. "Enough of these amateurs; let us look on Teo-teo! Stand up, Teo-teo, and bring us victory!"

But Teo-teo appeared in no hurry to stand up. Unobserved, he had moved back to the edge of the clearing and had there seated himself on a fallen coconut bole with his bow resting on the log beside him and the quiver drawn around between his knees. Nervously he turned his head from side to side, casting a look first at Queen Maemae and the throng surrounding her, then at the handful of archers still waiting. Once he peered over his shoulder at the now deserted path which led back to the village. One would have thought that the proud archer was seeking an avenue of escape; and in so thinking would have been correct. As everyone knows, it takes little courage to win, and for Teo-teo winning had always been easy. Now the specter of defeat stared him in the face and he quailed. Yet he was afraid to run, even as he was now afraid to compete, and so remained irresolute, his hands moving aimlessly over the rough surface of the coconut trunk at his either side.

The sound of the conch shell rang once more through the valley, and at this signal that it was now the turn of the champion and sole remaining hope of Tahiti, those who lined the field rose as one man. From side to side of the green hills the deep blast rocketed till the echoes were drowned by a shout which came from a thousand throats. "Teo-teo! Teo-teo!"

Where was the great man? Where the defender of the honor and prowess of King Tumu-nui's archers, the shining warrior who would humble the bold representative of Huahine? Where? The raised platform remained empty. No one approached. A perplexed and uneasy hush fell upon the Tahitians.

It seemed to Rata that it was but a moment ago that Teo-teo had stood at his side, and it was with surprise he now discovered him gone. He scanned the open field, but there was no one to be seen save the attendants of the games. He searched the massed faces of the crowd. Teo-teo might well be there among the many, yet surely he would have been recognized. Then, chancing to turn, Rata espied the deflated hero sitting upon the log with legs stretched out before him, staring vacantly at his toes as though he had heard neither the summons of the trumpeting shell nor the imperative shouting of his name.

Rata strode to him quickly. "Come, man," he said. "They wait for you!" And he half lifted Teo-teo to his feet. It was then he noticed that the older man's legs were unsteady and that his face had assumed an unhealthy tinge of gray. "What is it?" he demanded. "Are you ill?"

Teo-teo was in fact ill, ill with fear, but he shook his head slowly and mumbled inaudibly.

"Have you taken of the fermented juice of the coconut?" Rata exclaimed with growing impatience. "You have the appearance of a drunken man." He pushed Teo-teo toward the field. "Pull yourself together, archer! We need you on this day." Together they walked to the coral platform, Rata's hand still firmly and steadyingly clasped about the other's arm. As Tahiti's last hope clambered up a welcoming roar came from the crowd, a roar which smote Teo-teo's ears with horrible impact. He staggered back and would have fallen had not the king's son been there to support him.

"Take heart!" Rata called before he turned away. "You will be long remembered." Little he knew how truly he spoke. For Teo-teo was in all truth to be long remembered throughout all the islands, but not, alas, with pride or pleasure.

The champion's eyes sought the far end of the field where marking flags waved blithely in the gentle wind, blithely and—so it appeared to him—tantalizingly, mockingly. Had he once sent a shaft so far? As he raised his bow he felt his muscles had turned to water. The weapon trembled in his hands, trembled so that even distant watchers marked it with alarm. He clutched the arrow and string in his fingers; he pulled them back till the bow was at most half drawn . . . then a strange thing happened. It was a thing so strange that for a full minute after, the onlookers could not understand, could not believe. Teo-teo was talking to himself: "You are bettered," he muttered. "It is no use; you cannot win—no use, no use." Abruptly his will snapped and his fingers loosed the bow-string. Feebly, waveringly the arrow traveled a bare hundred yards, then fell dispiritedly to earth, short of the cast of even the meanest contestant.

Gaping, stunned, the people stared. But when at last they found tongue it was to give voice to a bellow of rage. Betrayed! Betrayed by the man on whom they had pinned their utmost faith. "Step down!" they cried. "Hide your face and your shame, miserable man! Away, away!"

Teo-teo stumbled from the field while the scathing taunts and insults continued to ring in his ears. "Return to the games of children, proud one filled with wind and empty boasts! Make of your bow a pole for the catching of crabs that walk on land!" And so it was that for ever after the word "teo-teo" came to mean all that is vanity and self-conceit.

It was now late afternoon, but for some while Rata had been so intent upon the fortunes of the erstwhile champion that his own doubts and uncertainties and his own impending trial had completely slipped his mind. It was all brought back to him suddenly and forcefully.

With the populace finally somewhat quieted, the master of the games, standing in the center of the grounds, cupped hands to his mouth. "Ehoma!" he cried, "Friends—one more challenger remains: Rata, Prince of Tahiti!"

Loyal cheers greeted this announcement, although few, if any, of those present held the slightest hope that their young prince, now entering a meet for the first time in his life, could snatch victory from what appeared complete and crushing defeat. Yet in the breasts of many a spark of pride glowed as they watched him mount the triangle of blocks dug from the sea to stand, tall and firm and determined, with the crimson ura feathers about his middle fluttering in the breeze. Here, however he might acquit himself as an archer, was the figure of a king!

Was this place, Rata asked himself, but four feet above the waving green expanse of the field? Queerly, he felt as though he looked down on all his people from a great height, from a cloud or a mountain, from a pinnacle where the air was cool and thin and intoxicating. There, not far away, were the grouped faces of his friends, his relatives, his father's subjects. Sitting among them, in a small circle kept respectfully cleared, was his own mother, with Turia at her side. Why, then, this sense of being at a great distance, as if he stood not upon a small stage reserved for archers, but upon the summit of once volcanic Orofena, the tallest of Tahiti's many peaks? Why? Because you are alone, Rata—alone with a task before you in which no man can help. Are you, too, to disappoint the waiting, trusting throng? Have you yourself been "teo-teo" in building this bow which you call Star-that-flies-by-night?

Slowly Rata removed the bow from his shoulder, and as he did so a murmur of wonder and surprise rose into the air. Never before had such a weapon been seen in the island world. The long, gracefully tapering span of polished wood glistened like the smooth green waters which fringed the island; it caught and reflected the rays of the sun as does the finest pearl shell. "What beauty! What grandeur!" fell the exclamations from many lips. "But who shall draw it?" questioned others. "Does our prince think to be a giant grown, or perhaps a godling?"

In this moment, however, Rata's thoughts were not upon himself. His eyes were turned to the far end of the field. There, though he still stood in brilliant light, the inland mountains now cast deep blue pools of shadow. It was shadow which moved and billowed as the wind

41

passed over the grass, shadow dotted with the white specks of marking flags. . . . But *were* those flags? Or were they whitecaps . . . ? Was that dipping, undulating grass—or was it the restless, heaving sea? A feeling of unreality seized Rata, and a momentary dizziness caused him to sway slightly where he stood. Were those trees which jutted upward where the valley clearing merged again with steep-sided jungle, or were they *masts?* The masts of ships! The masts of three majestic war-canoes riding slowly, serenely, wrapped in silence, with outspread matting sails. And where to? Where bound? To the valley's bitter end where darkness formed, where night began. How blurred and indistinct they seemed! At times like wraiths of smoke, like wisps of vagrant cloud, like moon-mist, pendant sea spray on a coral reef, shadows in a grotto on the ocean floor. Yet it was the war fleet of King Tumu-nui and there were figures on the decks and in the shrouds. The helmsman's platform towered at the stern—but where was Hoa Pahi? Rata's breath halted. Where was the great steering oar which he had held in his mighty grip? The vessel was rudderless; there was no sign of the Friend-of-the-Ship. And his father . . . ? Ah, there he was!

Tumu-nui, in full war regalia, the tall plumes of his helmet waving proud and free above his head, stood in the bow. Far as his father was, Rata could distinguish his noble, kindly features. Once before, many months ago, Rata had halted a swim for shore to turn and gaze back at a disappearing fleet. There the king had stood with feet firm-planted on the deck, eyes bent to what adventure no man could tell. So the former ruler of Tahiti now appeared in his son's vision: eyes forward, fearless of whatever fate lay hidden beyond the approaching night. Then he turned so that the glances of father and son met. He raised aloft the shattered remnant of a long, sharp-bladed lance. Words, whisper faint, sounded in Rata's ears.

"I have no want of this, son, on the journey which I go." With a sweep of his arm the king cast the broken spear away. There was a smile on his lips, yet they appeared not to move. "One weapon only do I need."

"Yes . . . ?"

"One weapon only: the love of those I leave behind. Let the arrow you hold carry that to me."

All unconscious, Rata had drawn a four-foot arrow from his

quiver and held the crimson-dyed shaft close to the tuft of yellow feathers. He fitted it to the bowstring. "You are so far away, my father," he thought.

"How far is night from day?" King Tumu-nui replied. "How far is the homeland, our final resting place? How far the gods from mortal men? Are they not all about you, in the breeze that fans your face, in the flowers which grow about your feet, in the warm rain that falls and the sun that shines?"

"*So far*," Rata's thoughts repeated.

"Love thinks nothing of such a distance," came the whispered answer.

Kneeling at the edge of the archer's platform, Rata raised the bow before him. Back came his strong right arm, back swiftly, surely, un-haltingly till the feathers at the arrow's nock brushed his cheek, till the stout limbs of the bow arc'd back in a half circle about him—till Star-that-flies-by-night was full drawn. He loosed the string. With the whirring rush of a flight of birds the blood-red bolt shot into the evening air. Up and up it went, caught flame-like in the leveling rays of the setting sun. To all who witnessed, Rata's arrow appeared a living thing impelled by a force no man-made bow could give. On and on it winged its way, soaring high above the sign of Teo-teo's forgotten triumph, high above the newly set stake of the man of Huahine.

Rata was on his feet. With pounding heart he watched the slender bamboo messenger glide like a glowing star down the sky passing from sunlight to twilight, to the haze of the middle valley, to shadow and then to deeper shadow where a waiting figure stood high in the prow of a Tahitian war canoe. King Tumu-nui stretched forth his arm. . . . He plucked the arrow from the air!

A great exultant roar burst from the crowd to crash and roll between the hills, and Rata brushed a hand across his eyes as does a man who comes awake. He looked about him, dazed. Why the insane clamor? Why should the formerly reasonably behaved spectators be leaping up and down as if possessed, slapping each other's backs, shouting his name again and again?

A voice spoke at his elbow and he turned to find Tavae of Huahine standing beside him. "I am glad," the man said, "to lose to such an archer. This day will be spoken of by our children's children and by theirs."

43

Men were racing over the field to its farthest extremity. There, at the edge of the clearing where forest and jungle began, was Rata's scarlet arrow, its head imbedded in a fallen mango tree. One of the tree's branches, still heavy with foliage, jutted upward from the prostrate trunk. It was curious. One might have taken it for a mast and sail.

VII

THERE is an hour before dawn, before first cock-crow, when the cool Tahitian darkness is most intense. The faint light of stars fails to penetrate the blanket which lies heavily black over mountains and silent valleys and within the groves of coconut palms where fronds hang inert, their daytime rustling murmur stilled. The dried brown thatching of the houses which line the grassy, dew-wet streets merges with the night, and those within then sleep the soundest. All things slumber: the winds, the sea which stirs but lazily against the reefs, the clouds anchored motionless against Orofena's highest slopes.

What then of the man, alone of all living creatures, who at such a time strode through the dark, his feet finding unerringly the trail leading upward to the cliff which looked out on pass and bay? What drew him from his rest at this hour when even the tides pause in their ebb and flow? Could it be that Rata still held hope; that again, as on how many hundred days past, he would stand sentinel to the rising sun while he tried vainly to quiet his pulse hurrying with stubborn expectancy?

No, on this morning it was not as before. He seated himself where once long ago he had looked down on a war fleet floating in the harbor below, where he had stood with strings of breadfruit swinging at either end of the pole he carried while his eyes devoured the scene of feverish preparation. Adventure it had meant then; adventure in which he, too, craved a part. No other thought had entered his mind. How young he must have been on that distant day! And young he had remained till —till when? Until yesterday upon the field of archers.

Through how many months had he made the solitary pilgrimage to this lofty cliff? How many times had he waited alone for the dawn, feeling each time a near certainty that surely *this* breaking day would disclose three fine ships returning home to safe harbor? He had lost all count. Always the first gray light showed the same monotonous and expressionless face of the empty sea. Always he saw the same virgin waste, unscarred as though never a vessel had blazed a path thereon. He did not know why he came again to his post, for though he sat as before with his eyes turned oceanward where the long swells still hid in the moist darkness, he looked for nothing, expected nothing. No longer did he pray for the night to raise quickly its obscuring mantle, or for the sun to hurry its ascent. Let the shadows linger, let night drag on and day come with whatever slow unconcern. It did not matter; King Tumu-nui would not return.

There had been feasting and celebration following the archers' meet and the king's house was filled with the chiefs and nobles of surrounding villages come to congratulate the winner of the games. As always happens when Tahitians gather, there had been innumerable lengthy speeches. Each man had seemed determined to outdo the next in eloquent praise of Rata's feat, but during it all Rata had sat quietly beside his mother, and if one had looked closely, as did Queen Maemae more than once, he would have seen that the young man's thoughts were far away. Yet once a smile touched Rata's lips when his uncle began passing the bow from hand to hand that all might see its length and girth and try its strength. "You see, you see?" Iore kept proudly repeating. "He is in truth my sister's son!"

The hour was late when the last of the visitors departed and now, despite the fresh outside air, Rata's eyelids were heavy. Finally they closed. It could have been but minutes that he slept, yet the troubled dream which pursued him seemed interminable:

He is walking, endlessly walking through a dim world of greenish light. Walking, but with what strange effort! The air is heavy, liquid, and he puts out his hands to part it, brush it aside. I must pass, he keeps thinking, I must push on through all this greenness; I must keep on till I have found the thing I seek. Yet what is that thing? Why am I here and why do I struggle with this cool, embracing fluid which folds about me, lifting me like a feather, yet dragging like a weight at arms and legs? Why and what for? Is this soft, melting stuff of green for man to breathe . . . ? Never mind; it fills the lungs most easily. Push on,

Rata; keep searching. There is no rest till you have found it. See—here are lovely rolling hills covered with flowering shrubs of tender blue and green; here are stately, vine-clad cliffs filled with a thousand tiny grottoes, the nesting place of birds. And there are the birds themselves in all their myriad rainbow colors. But how queer their flight. For minutes they hang suspended in the luminous green, then dip and weave in lazy circles, dreamily and silent. Silent! What sort of fowls are these? Look closely, Rata. Look once again. Not birds, but fish! Fish with trailing, feather-like plumes, fish yellow as the wild thrush, scarlet as the mountain duck, purple and blue as whistling parakeets. And these delicate, spidery shrubs of rose and ivory, these forests of towering toadstools with spreading, convoluted tops like the bared brains of giants turned to stone, these overhanging amber walls with twisting veins of turquoise and dull gold—are they corals all? Rata pauses in wonder and stares above. Then those clouds which float slowly across the heavens, are they but huge, white-bellied sharks? And the seeming winged things whose thick and fleshy, indolently flapping pinions cast so dark a shadow—are they but mantas, the greatest of the rays? Yes, yes: and this is not the world of living men!

But if that is so, who is this old woman who sits at a crossing of watery ways between the many valleys? Infinitely old she is, with bowed stalks of legs, curling thin-boned arms and tenuous, trailing finger tips. Old, old, yet long hair of smoky black floats about her sunken eyes and hollow cheeks like the night-dark screening cloud an octopus spews forth. Does a pareu faintly shroud her skeletal form? If so, it is woven of the green, translucent stuff of the sea itself. But what madness is this? The creature is seated by a pile of stones: a native oven. And surely it is a breadfruit which she tosses in her tremulous hands, slapping it to soften it as women have done since Tahiti was first settled. Why does the ancient dame sway as if caught in the rhythm of some solemn, long-forgotten dance? What does she here . . . ?

"Well might I ask the same question, Rata of Tahiti," says the old woman. "What do *you* here where lie only those whom the sea has swallowed?"

"I am hunting," he replies, "hunting everywhere for I know not what."

"Then cease your labors; go search in the air above."

"But what is it that I seek—can you tell me that?"

"Yes," she answers without ceasing her languid, spineless dance, "I can if.I am so minded."

"Then 'tell me!" he exclaims. "Tell me and receive my thanks!"

"Today, my son, you dream."

"Of course," he breaks in. "I know. This is a dream. Just a dream. A dream, nothing more."

"Yesterday you saw a vision."

"That I did," he agrees in mounting excitement. "You are right, old mother. Go on, go on! Tell me more."

"Your father's fleet passed before your eyes and you beheld each man who with him sailed—each man save one."

"True. Yes, true!"

"It is that one you seek, Rata."

He stands staring straight before him. Then his fogged sight and his brain, dulled with weariness, seem to clear. He is gazing at a vaguely stirring ocean fern. In its midst, gently lifting in some vagrant current, caressed by the soft brown fronds, is a round, creamy yellow sea-porcupine. But the voice of the witching plant still echoes in his ears: ". . . each man save one."

Suddenly he cried aloud, "Hoa Pahi, it is you!" And with a start he was awake, the light of dawn filling his wide eyes.

VIII

THE NIGHT was gone and birds were already in flight. No muted, cold-blooded creatures these, but true birds whose hearts beat warm and fast, whose music greeted morning. The clouds, torn from their resting place by winds aloft, streamed out from Orofena with edges set aflame by a sun still hidden behind the dark blue mountain. *Real* clouds—no things of water-breathing gills with hides of frozen grit and sand, but fleecy soft and made to feed on air.

Rata looked out upon the sea where Orofena still cast its massive shadow. Then he bounded to his feet. Something floated just beyond the harbor's mouth! Not a ship, not a war canoe, but something which lay low and practically awash upon the tranquil waters. Impatiently he glanced above and behind. "O great Mahana!—great Sun, come quickly and flood the world with brilliant light!" Was it only a bit of driftwood, a twisting centipede-like branch from a coconut palm, a rotted and discarded dugout? Ah—at last! The sun shot above the peak, burned down upon the barrier reef and the ocean beyond. It disclosed with merciless clarity a grim and desolate scene. A single human form lay there supported, apparently, by a half submerged log. It was a form which raised no voice, no hand, to hail the shore. Except for a limp rocking from side to side as the swells rose and fell away, it did not move. Yet there was movement near by. Two shell-white swallows frolicked through the transparent air, diving, turning, always in perfect unison. Twice they dipped low, grazing the unheeding castaway with their wings, then darted off on their gay, erratic way seeking other sport. Perhaps it was the sight of them, the embodiment of all that is joyous, alive and free, which caused Rata to feel the sudden stab of fear.

He raised hands to his mouth and shouted down on the village housetops. "Men of Tahiti! Throw off your sleep. Awake, fishermen and warriors; awake and launch canoes!" Without waiting to see the effect of his words, he plunged into the narrow, winding trail which led below. As he ran the people stumbled dazedly, still heavy with sleep, from the open doorways. What could have caused the sudden alarm? Had the plundering marauders of Vavau again descended upon them in the night? Women clutched their children to them fearfully, men poured into the streets with spears and war clubs in their hands. To right and left they looked but saw no foe.

A moment later Rata burst into the village. "The pass!" he cried. "To the pass!" and without pausing he raced on to the cove and his own canoe.

Their eyes turned seaward and a moan like a low sighing of wind escaped them at the sight they saw. Instinctively each knew that the inert, sea-rocked figure was a cast-off remnant of King Tumu-nui's band. Had but a single man returned to speak for a company of hundreds?

Rata grasped his dugout by the stern, shot it over the sloping strip of sand onto the lagoon and leaped aboard. With long sweeps of the paddle he sent the light craft bounding forward, each powerful stroke lifting high the bow and pointed outrigger. He was halfway to the reef when other canoes pushed off from all along the curving beach. The entire lagoon now shimmered in sunlight and the many speeding little vessels of thin-shelled mango, purau and breadfruit logs had an ironically sportive, even festive air. Yet this was no day of games, when snatches of song and laughter cross the water, no mere test of swiftness or endurance. A race, yes, but a race against death itself and, save for the swish of fast-dipping paddles, a silent one.

Rata's canoe, hastened still more by the outbound current, slid through the pass. For a brief instant he was abreast of the green combers which pawed lazily, with a deep rumbling, at the coral heads on either side, then he was on the sea beyond. No further need to ask himself, nor his dreams, who lay there just ahead. No need to ask what was that precarious life-raft. It was Hoa Pahi, lashed by his waistcloth to his own tiller, his chest and head and outflung arms resting on the wide blade of the rudder and his legs floating against the long, straight shaft behind. Hoa Pahi—yet as Rata swung alongside a doubt shot through his mind and he stared in momentary unbelief. Could it be? Could this haggard skeleton be the same man who had stood so solidly, so rugged and strong beside the king on all his voyages? Could this be the man who had tossed Rata in his arms, even when Tumu-nui's son was a half-grown boy, as if he were no heavier than a coconut? Each bone in his body stood out as though it would pierce the skin. Each tendon in the wasted arms and legs showed clear like strained, taut sennit cord. The tangled, matted hair clung close to the shrunken skull. But the lips—ah, those wide, homely lips, baked and cracked as they were by salt and sun, were not to be mistaken.

"You have come back, beloved friend," Rata murmured. "Tauhere, you have come back to me." And only half restraining his sobs he knelt in his canoe and bent above his father's trusted steersman. When he grasped the maro of beaten bark the rotted cloth fell away in his hands. Oro be thanked for these calm waters! If the sea had been higher not even the body of Hoa Pahi would ever have returned to Tahiti. And was this but a body, a corpse? It felt cold to Rata's touch and there was a grayish tinge to the puckered skin. Still lower Rata bent till his cheek was close to the man's mouth. Faint, ever so faint, was the breath which came haltingly, uncertainly from Hoa Pahi's once powerful lungs. Yet breath there was, and Rata straightened with a cry of hope.

"He lives!" he shouted to his uncle Iore, whose canoe came on before the others. "Make haste, make haste!"

Iore, that tall and bony man, drove his outrigger forward with quick strokes, and in another minute he was at Rata's side. He looked down at the castaway. "What poor wretch have we here?"

"Who but Hoa Pahi," Rata replied.

"Hoa Pahi!" Iore exclaimed, looking closer. "But it is, it is! Where, then, are the others? Where is Tumu-nui? What . . . ?"

"Stop not now for fruitless talk," said Rata almost harshly, "but stretch forth your arms and help me lift him to my canoe. There is no time to lose, or Hoa Pahi will never live to answer your questions."

Together they raised the unconscious man, drew him over the gunwale and laid him gently in the bottom of Rata's dugout. Iore left his canoe to be picked up by the others and took his place in the bow. The two paddles bit the water and they headed back. From canoe to canoe the word traveled, till it reached the waiting throng on the strand. "It is Hoa Pahi! It is King Tumu-nui's helmsman, the strongest of his warriors. Hoa Pahi alone, alone of all the many, has returned!" And although the unmoving lips of the Friend-of-the-Ship held the secret of the expedition's fate, there was no soul in the village who did not know in that minute that the loved ones gone with Tumu-nui would never again be seen.

When Rata and Iore stepped ashore carrying their burden between them, the crowd pressed close, staring fascinated, filled with awe and pity by the shrunken form which was Hoa Pahi. Many were the tear-stained faces of mothers and young girls, even of fathers and old men, all thinking of lovers, sons or husbands who had sailed away so cheerfully confident with the steersman and his king.

"You must let us pass," said Rata. "We carry him to my mother, who will bring him back to health if it lies in human hands to do so."

They made a path, and Rata and Iore went on, but there were some so carried away by their sorrow that they continued to impede the progress of the two men, some who followed close beside them imploring, beseeching for news which neither one could give. A young girl, beautiful even in her grief, her long, dark hair disheveled, broke through and grasped one of Hoa Pahi's hands, which swung limply at his side. "Speak!" she cried. "Speak to me, Hoa Pahi! Rai—Rai who loves me, whose lips were so warm on mine—where is he now? Where does he rest his head when the night is dark?" She threw herself upon the ship-wrecked man and pressed her face to his cold cheek. "Hoa Pahi, *speak* to me!"

Rata caught the eye of an old woman who stood near and she, understanding his glance, came forward and, gently disengaging the dis-

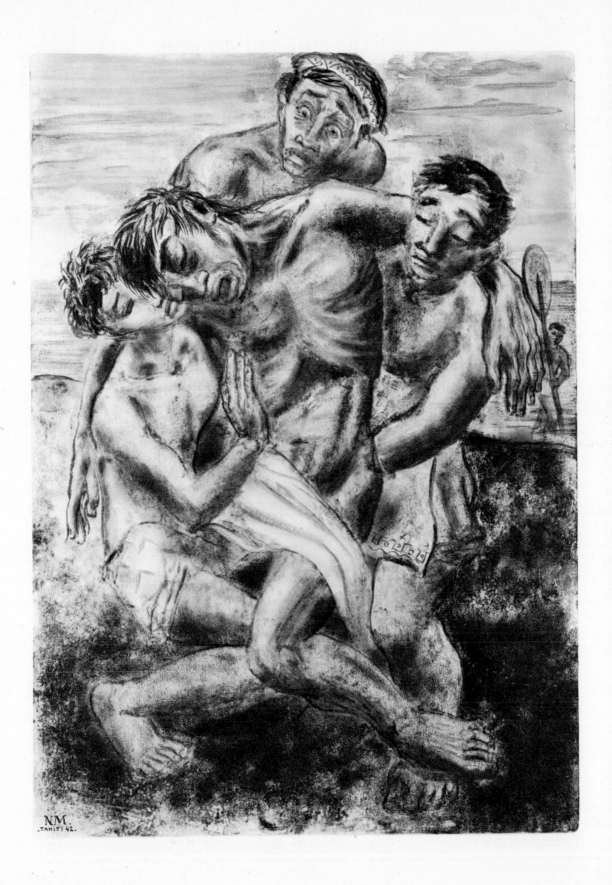

tracted girl's arms from about Hoa Pahi, led her, still weeping, away.

The news had quickly reached the palace, so that when Rata and Iore entered they found sleeping mats ready placed. They lowered Hoa Pahi to the clean pandanus, and Turia came immediately with coverings of tapa which she drew over him. Rata's mother knelt beside the stricken one; she felt of his wrists, lifted one of his eyelids.

"Will he recover?" Rata demanded anxiously.

The Queen appeared not to have heard him. "Turia," said she, "place drinking nuts here at my side. And oil and herbs."

"Will he walk again?" Rata insisted.

His mother turned her eyes up to him. "If we need you, Rata, we will call. Go now with your uncle Iore."

The two men left the house, and outside they separated, Rata to stroll disconsolately down to the shore again. Here he found a pair of canoes nosing into the sand. Borne across the gunwales was the heavy tiller of his father's ship.

"Let it be placed beneath the eaves of the king's house," he dirrected; and, turning south along the beach, he left the village.

How far he walked alone with his gloomy thoughts he did not know, but it was late afternoon when he found himself standing on a rocky peninsula which jutted into the sea from a part of the coast where there was no off-lying reef. Combers rode in unimpeded, to dash foaming at his feet, covering him at each impact with their cool spray. Here was no placid green lagoon but the deep blue of the vast, encircling ocean, no bathing place for children with their boats and toys, but the high sea against which only men might pit their strength. And in this even kings succumbed! Was it this restless, heaving monster, which even now shook the ground beneath his feet, that had brought his father to his death? What a mockery, then, became revenge. Rata shook his head. Can one grapple with the gods of the sea as one would with an octopus, an eel or a wild boar? He laughed harshly. Can one seize upon and punish nature itself? Would you, he asked himself bitterly, do battle with all that is evil in the world at large?

"Yes!" he shouted with sudden defiance. "Yes! That I would do!" His words were lost in the spume and he turned his face upwards. "Give me the strength, O great Oro!"

High in the clear evening sky a single man-of-war bird wheeled in slow, majestic circles. "Listen to me, shadow of the supreme god," he cried again, his eyes fixed on the soaring speck in the blue. "Give me the strength—give me thrice the strength of common mortals. Show me the evil that stalks the earth and sea to bring good men to an untimely end; show it to me in form that I may perceive, touch, feel. Let me thrust, stab, slash and spear and destroy it utterly!"

Was it a sign? Or was it but the way of that plunderer of the skies? The bird flipped up one of its wings and then, with a speed the eye could hardly follow, dove toward the rocky point on which Rata stood. There was a momentary break in the scud which drenched the ground about his feet, and Rata saw a booby rise from the water with a fish in its mouth. Upward the foolish creature flew, swallowing its meal as it went, all unaware of the lightning descent of the man-of-war bird. All unaware till the last frightened moment when it cocked its head to see the menace. Hastily, obediently, the booby disgorged the newly swallowed fish, and in full flight, with long curved beak, the bird of Oro snapped it up. Then, satisfied, the robber flew away on leisured wings, and the booby went back to its hungry search.

A sign? Perhaps. A sign that the beautiful world of Oro is also a cruel world where each living thing hunts and is hunted, preys and is preyed upon in turn. But an answer to his fervent prayer? Again Rata shook his head. He did not know, and with his thoughts still dark and troubled he started back toward the distant village.

The light faded swiftly from the sky as he went. Yet Rata was hardly conscious whether it was night or day. He left behind the rocky strip of coast with its angry seas, and soon his feet touched again the smooth sands where the shielded lagoon waters rise and fall with no more than a sibilant whisper. The birdcalls were stilled, the trade wind died away and gave place to a barely perceptible draft of air which floated down from the cooling mountain slopes. In Tumu-nui's village the evening fires would be lighting to broil the fish and bake the roots of taro. Rata walked through the dusk, alone with the memory of his father and with his fears and hopes for the faithful steersman. He walked slowly and twice he stopped for long moments to watch the stars growing, brightening in the tropic air. It was as if he would delay as long as possible the return to his home, dreading the news that might await him there. Did Hoa Pahi's stout heart still beat; did breath still move within the wasted frame? Rata seemed to hear again the anguished cry of the girl beseeching word of her sweetheart: "Rai—where is he, where does he rest . . . ? Hoa Pahi, speak to me!" How willingly would Rata have echoed those words. Speak, Hoa Pahi, and tell me of my father. On whom, on what, must I avenge his death? Tell me, that I may make ready and set out to whatever distant land or sea.

It was late when he stood without the low-arched door through which Tumu-nui had passed so many times. Once more the village slept, but in the king's house someone kept a vigil; faint light showed through the chinks of the plaited bamboo walls. Rata paused on the threshold. The helm of the flagship lay propped to one side of the lintel, and he passed a hand slowly over its rugged length, stooping to touch the thick blade which had divided so many leagues of trackless ocean, then letting his palm slide up till he felt the smooth-worn depression where Hoa Pahi had held the paddle lovingly, caressingly, in days of fair sailing, where he had gripped and fought when the tiller bounded and struggled like a thing alive in times of gale and storm. A thing alive? How inert it seemed now, how inanimate, how out of place beneath these sheltering eaves on this dry land. Somehow it served to bring home to Rata for the first time the immensity of his loss, the awfulness of the disaster. His head swam and a momentary weakness assailed him, so that he clutched the stout shaft for support. But it left him as quickly as it came, and strength flowed back into his body. Tumu-nui, the beloved, was gone but there was still a king in Tahiti. A king does not bow to the blows of fate. A king strikes out, commands, attacks!

His grasp tightened on the weathered helm. "You shall taste anew the salt brine," he muttered, his voice low and vibrant. "You shall breathe afresh the tempest and the tumult of the deep; you shall live again!" He let his arm fall to his side and entered the house.

Turia and his mother, their hands—so long busied in his care—now resting quietly in their laps, were seated beside the outstretched figure of Hoa Pahi. Close by, a taper of carefully strung candlenuts threw faint reddish light over the silent little group.

Queen Maemae looked up at her tall son, then closed her eyes and nodded slowly. Rata understood. Hoa Pahi, too, would live to sail the seas again.

Without speaking, he walked to the far end of the house, threw himself down in the shadows on his mat of pandanus leaf and fell immediately into an exhausted slumber.

IX

URING the two months which followed an amazing thing took place, a thing of which the people of the south seas have never ceased to speak with wonder. In the space of sixty days Rata shot up to a height such that he was head and shoulders above the tallest man in all Tahiti. His strength increased till he was the equal of any three warriors ever known. The word spread over the seas. Tavae, the archer, returning to his own country, carried it to Huahine. From there it traveled to Vavau, to Tahaa, to Havai'i, even to the most remote and thinly populated atolls. It went with such swiftness that many claimed no human messenger was responsible but rather the winds, the birds, the scudding clouds.

Sun-bronzed fishermen dropped their spears and pearl-shell lures, canoe-builders threw down their adzes, old women ceased their gossip and laid aside the wooden mallets with which they beat cloth from mulberry bark, young girls left babes in the care of the smallest children and all gathered to hear again and again the marvelous tale: Oh, listen to the wonder the gods have wrought. Harken while we tell of Oro's gift to great Tahiti; hear, friends, of the new king of all that mighty island, the son and heir of Tumu-nui. Rata is his name and a *giant* king is he! His bow is of a sapling formed; his war club none but he can wield. His strength is as the strength of three.

So the incredible story went; and yet in it there was little enough of exaggeration. For the bow with which Rata had won the archers' meet now appeared to him a mere plaything. The clubs and spears of other men were, in his hands, no more than brittle toys. But despite the remarkable change which he had undergone in so short a time, Rata's character remained unaltered. He displayed no unseemly pride in his superhuman prowess. It was only rarely, and then at the insistence of chiefs and nobles, that he would consent to move with one hand canoes which required a group of men for launching or to cast boulders far to sea as if they were so many pebbles. His miraculous strength, Rata felt, was not given him for sport nor for the amusement and edification of the curious. It was a gift of Oro, of that no doubt; and it was a gift bestowed for a reason and a purpose. What that purpose was Rata kept locked within his breast, where he held the treasured memory of his father.

Two people alone of all those who then walked upon the islands fully realized that he lived and grew but to exact a vengeance. Neither of these took comfort in the knowledge; rather it was yet another cause for apprehension and foreboding.

Turia could remember well the evening of Hoa Pahi's return when she, with Queen Maemae, had sat watching at the sick man's side. Rata had entered with his newly formed resolve—and she had sensed it instantly. Oh, how strong then had been the temptation to cry out. "Not you, Rata," she would have implored. "Think not to follow in their path; there has been enough of death. Let be!" Yet she had held her peace and, though their common sorrow had brought them more and more frequently together, so she had continued to do during all the long days of the helmsman's slow recovery. Once, when the king's fleet still rode above the waves, she had mildly chided him: "Like Tani, you think the seas made alone for sport and play!" But that was long ago. Time had passed and Rata was now as mature as she. Even had he spoken, she could have known no better the grimness of his determination.

With clairvoyance of a different sort, with her unerring mother's instinct, Queen Maemae was equally aware that Rata would one day sail for the horizon, and that when that day came there would be no holding him. It was still her fancy, regardless of the smiles of her retainers, to call him her tamarii—her little boy—but words could not alter the fact that he was now a king, master of his destiny and waiting only the ceremony of coronation to make him master as well of the destinies of all other Tahitians. A deep sadness came to her eyes at these thoughts. Time passed so swiftly, the world changed so fast. One day Tumu-nui was by her side still in the prime of life; then he was gone and the son sprung from his loins was in his stead. "May he rule wisely," she would pray. "May he rule well and generously as his father." Then, in answer to fearful afterthought: "Oh, may he *live* to rule! Let it not be again the same." If only she could know what lay ahead.

THE SHIP OF FLAME

For Queen Maemae, even as Rata himself, was still in ignorance of what he must combat. Not yet had Hoa Pahi's lips told the story of that dreadful day when all the fleet was lost. "Wait," he had answered Rata's frequent questions. "Wait until all the people hail you king; wait for the day of ceremony when priests and chiefs bow down, for the day when the twin sharks come in from sea to touch your flesh. Then come to me. And you shall know." Darkness lurked thick in the helmsman's eyes at such times, and often Queen Maemae asked herself on what awful scene of destruction and death the Friend-of-the-Ship had looked. But if Rata, listening quietly, read aught in Hoa Pahi's glance, he gave no sign.

THE TWO MONTHS which had passed contained such concentrated activity as had not been seen in a generation. A king was to be made. But no ordinary king this—a giant king for whom the drums must beat louder, the fires burn higher, the feasting last longer, the songs and chants rise more beautiful than ever before. To work, men and women of Tahiti! To work, that visitors from far-off kingdoms may be dazzled by the splendor of Rata's coronation, that it may be remembered, told and sung, through the ages to come when we who toiled are forgotten dust. Cultivate the fields that the ovens may be filled to bursting; beat out the choicest bark of purau, that ornamented capes may adorn the shoulders of our chiefs; adze out new canoes, that the old may light the fires of the sacred marae; hunt out the rare wild duck, that another row of feathers may be added to the royal girdle marking the beginning of a new reign. Priests!—weed carefully the temple grounds, fast, pray and stand vigil through the nights, invoke the hosts of gods, that the days of Rata may be prosperous. Youths and maidens, bards and jesters, all you of the society Arioi!—prepare your pageants, your music and your dances, weave your garlands of sweet jasmine and gardenia, come with flowers in your hair, about your throats, your wrists and ankles, that there may be laughter and merriment and good cheer.

Thus it had been in Tahiti while two moons went through their courses from narrow crescent to full orb. Now at last it was done, the representatives of the far-flung islands had arrived, all was in readiness. The sun rose in a burst of riotous color above Orofena, and at the same time the thudding of sacred drums rolled throughout the land. The glorious day had begun.

Rata turned on his mat and opened his eyes. He sat up and shook his head to drive out the sleep from his brain. Then he saw that Hoa Pahi was seated on the sand floor but a few paces away and that the steersman regarded him smiling. It struck him that Hoa Pahi looked, on this morning, very much like his old, vigorous self. Was this not the first time a smile had touched those wide lips since his return? As far as Rata's knowledge went, it was.

"You are amused, good friend," he said.

"Yes," Hoa Pahi replied, "for some time while you slept I have been watching you, and I have been thinking. I could not help but smile."

"Was I then sleeping with mouth wide like a trap for lizards?"

"No, not that. I was thinking and remembering; remembering a time not so long past when we used to call you fledgling, youngster, even stripling—a time when it still irked you sorely to be thought a youth and you yearned to be a man and twice a man." Hoa Pahi paused; his eyes circled the room, then returned to Tumu-nui's son. "Well," he finished, "your wishes have been granted. You have come of age as you desired, and your shoulders are broader than those of any man I ever saw." The smile left his rugged features. "It is well they should be, for you will find heavy tasks lie ahead."

Rata did not reply immediately and a silence fell between the two men, not an uneasy silence, but one of understanding. Yes, Rata realized, it was true that he had come of age. In the eyes of his countrymen he had reached man's estate on the day when he stood upon the raised platform of the archers' field and loosed an arrow which proved to one and all that he was more than the equal of the best. He had borne himself like a warrior, hence such he was considered forever onward as long he he might live. And in Rata's own mind, also, that day marked the beginning of his majority—but for a very different reason. Others had seen him carry off a victory. None could know that he also carried from the field the certainty that he stood alone in his father's place.

So what of the responsibilities, the "heavy tasks" of which Hoa Pahi now spoke? Were not such things ever the accompaniment of growth? Were they not to be looked forward to when one laid aside the ways of youth, to be sought eagerly, ardently, to be faced with high heart? Rata had always thought so, even as he did today.

"I shall be ready, Hoa Pahi," he made answer at last, "ready for whatever the gods may have in store."

"That is well," said the older man, getting to his feet. "Tonight, while the others feast and revel in your honor, we shall talk together earnestly and long." He stepped close and placed a hand on the young sovereign's arm. "I shall be beside you throughout the ceremony, and never shall I have walked with one more fit to be a king. But now I go. Bathe and prepare yourself, for soon your mother and her attendants will come to anoint you with scented oil and to wrap about you the white maro woven by the hands of the high priest."

X

THE SUN had reached the zenith and blazed down upon the great verdant island, casting hardly a shadow, when at last there came again the deep, resonant sound of the temple drums. Now the tempo was steady, measured, echoing back from the hills with an insistent booming which beat against the ears with a throbbing pressure. It seemed to the hearers like the heavy pulse of their own blood. And so it was, in a way, for the waves of sound coming from the hollowed logs with their taut heads of leather-like shark skin were truly the voice of this people filling the air, filling each cranny of the sprawling village, each dark corner of the shaded marae, each skull hanging on the temple walls. It filled, too, every living soul, making itself one with his heartbeats, one with his spirit, one with his very being. It welded the assembled multitude, fused them into a single whole, intent upon a single earnest purpose. An ancient race was about to raise a king on high.

Heralded by the blasts of twenty conch shells, a solemn procession entered the crowded capital. In the lead, carried by marae attendants known as nurses of the god, was the swaying feather-bedecked image of the terrible Oro. Immediately behind walked four chiefs of the realm bearing upon their shoulders a massive throne hewn from a solid block of hardest miro wood. Strong men they were and tall as it is fitting chiefs should be, yet they bent beneath their burden, for upon the carven throne sat no ordinary man but one whose weight was that of two. So Rata was borne aloft, his head surmounted by a long-plumed helmet, high above the surrounding sea of joyful faces. On his right hand strode the dauntless Hoa Pahi in full war dress, and on his left Iore, brother of the Queen. Then came a small and wizened man, his parchment skin creased by a hundred wrinkles: Tahua, high priest of Tahiti, followed by a long line of lesser priests and servants of the marae in the bleached maros and fringed capes which marked their holy office. It was an impressive, an awe-inspiring spectacle, and as the procession approached, the massed onlookers gave way to leave a wide and unimpeded path. Beat on, drums of Oro! Send out your rumbling, thundering message. Let it reach the farthest dim horizons, let it echo in the sky tunnels through which the four winds roar, let it reverberate in the passages through which rise the sun and moon, let all gods and men be aware: here comes a king!

Like a monster eel the long, slow-marching column wound through the streets, circled twice the royal dwelling and then turned into the broad, flower-bordered thoroughfare which led to the water. With eyes straight before him, Rata looked to the foot of the avenue where the lagoon glinted green in the sunlight. On its mirror surface he could see another procession no less brilliant than that in which he rode. A fleet of canoes, paddles dipping to the drumbeats, glided toward the shore. and the water-borne parade, too, twisted and turned in slow convolutions—a gaudy sea-serpent headed by the twin-hulled vessel intended to receive aboard both Oro and the new monarch. Anuanua, the first canoe was called—the rainbow—and rightly so, for it was arched with garlands of every flower which grew upon the land, with gardenias, jasmine, lilies, with bright yellow purau, purple-tinged ti and crimson-flaming hau. Amidships was raised a dais about which hung bright-dyed tassels of shredded bark and puppet-like effigies of the god of war. Round the head of each man aboard was bound a circlet of spear-shaped coconut leaves, and round each arm was fastened a sennit-braided

charm. The same mood of solemnity which marked the approaching procession ashore pervaded this sacred vessel.

But what a contrast were the numerous smaller outrigger canoes which followed in its wake! The boisterous, the irrepressible society of Arioi, the dancers and singers and fun-makers, filled them so that the gunwales were nearly awash. The Arioi respect no law, no tapu; their mission is but to bring laughter, music and love to an island which has enough of sorrow, death and tragedy. Clothed by no more than slender streamers of gold and russet leaves, flowers in their hair, they stand upright in the narrow canoes. They seize upon the measured throb of holy drums and take it to themselves. They clap hands, slap naked thighs, they double and redouble the slow, austere, recurring beat till it is a frenzied rhythm, till their sinuous bodies tremble and writhe in fevered dance. Look well, O Tahitians, and all men of foreign isles! Do you not perceive the ancient story we have to tell? Can you not see what our eyes and lips are saying, not read the message of our arms and hands and swaying hips? Does not the pulse of paddles striking our canoes set your blood afire? If not, then surely are you of the living dead who cannot hear, who cannot taste nor feel. It is of the joys and pleasures that we speak: of the perfume of flowers, of the flavor of fine foods, the magic of love, the beauties of sweet youth. We speak of the senses and of life. Ia ora na tatou—life to you all—and life to the coming king!

The two companies, the one from the land and the other from the sea, met on the sanded beach at a place where rose a tall pillar of white stone. Te-papa-o-ruea was the name of this rock of investment, and beside it the four chiefs laid down the heavy throne. Tahua grasped Rata's hand and the young man rose to follow the withered priest down to the lagoon. Out into the clear, warm waters they strode, Rata still clad in the plain white tapa waist cloth, the trailing fringes of the old man's cape floating out behind him.

"Kneel!" Tahua commanded in his high-pitched, quavering voice. "Kneel, my son, that the ocean may enfold you; clasp it as a brother that it may serve and not destroy you." The drums were hushed, and even the reckless Arioi quieted as Rata did as he was bidden.

Then, reedily, uncertainly, Tahua began to chant.

Arise, my king, from Moana, the dark blue sea;

THE SHIP OF FLAME

Arise to Tahiti of the peaceful Moon;
Draw the tens, and draw the thousands;
Arise, O Rata, and draw the whole of
Great Tahiti to thee!

Rata stood to his full height while rivulets ran from his bronzed back and arms to fall sparkling into the calm lagoon about him. He faced the pass, and cried out so that all the multitude crowding the shore could hear: "Come, shark-gods! Come, twin deities of the deep, and give me your greeting!"

The silence was now so complete that Rata could hear the faint plash of the drops which continued to fall from his firm-wound tapa. All eyes turned to the break in the barrier reef. All the assembled thousands waited for the inevitable sign that a true king, and no usurper, now ruled in the land. Minutes passed and no one moved. Like some stunted, weather-whipped tree, Tahua stood frozen with one gnarled hand raised to shade his eyes, but his sight was keener than all others, and at last he stretched out a skinny arm. "There," said he. "They have heard." Soon two fins were clear to everyone. They cut the water with barely a ripple, but moved swiftly and straight for the spot where Rata stood. Reaching him, the sharks whirled in circles, churning and whipping the water with their great tails so that king and priest were half hidden by spray; they gamboled and frolicked, swimming so close that they brushed Rata's legs and thighs. Then, swiftly as they had come, they turned and made for the open sea.

Once again the priest took his sovereign by the hand, and together they walked up onto the dry land to the foot of the white stone pillar where Tahiti's chiefs awaited. Here, ranged neatly upon mats spread on the sands, were the royal symbols. Tahua stooped and first picked up the tahiri—a great fan-spread of tail plumes from the man-of-war bird bound to the end of a long lance. "The symbol of peace; take it in your hands."

Rata did so, and then passed it on to Iore, who held it upright so that the plumes waved high above their heads.

"Take thy spear," Tahua went on, giving him the mighty weapon of toa wood, "the symbol of war and kin to the birds of the air." This, too, Rata accepted. Then he handed it to Hoa Pahi, who grasped it firmly.

A SAGA OF THE SOUTH SEAS

There remained at the feet of the priest the most sacred of all the royal emblems, the banyan cloth maro to which were attached with needles of human bone a thousand vivid quills from the wild ducks who haunt the mountain lakes. A slight breeze stirred the scarlet feathers so that the garment lying against the white pandanus mat seemed a mound of quivering, living fire.

Tahua gathered the long, foot-wide maro in his hands. "Gird on the maro of your ancestors," said he. "Gird on the maro whose angular design tells of the greatness of those who went before; gird on the sacred maro whose name is Glowing-Sky-of-Dawn. Thus are you made a king, and thus do you follow in glory and in splendor!" Reverently he wound it round and round Rata's waist so that when he was done a flaming strip hung down before and behind, almost touching the ground. For a moment Rata stood motionless in the blazing ornament, then he stepped to the throne and took his place upon it.

The four chiefs lifted it on high and a deafening shout of acclaim came from the people. Those on shore and those on the water raised their hands. "Maeva Arii!" they cried again and again. "Hail, King, hail! Hail, Rata, King of all Tahiti!"

XI

IT WAS LATE EVENING before the last of the ceremonies was completed, before the fleet of the Arioi and the canoe of Oro had made the circuit of the lagoon bearing both Rata and the image of the god, before the last rites and sacrifices were done within the most tapu grounds of the marae. But with the setting of the sun the regal trappings were laid carefully away, and men donned their ordinary clothing. Torches were lighted, the stone ovens were uncovered and the savory odors of roast pig and fowl, fish and breadfruit drifted through the streets of the capital. The Arioi took charge. Till break of day the feasting, the merriment and rejoicing would continue.

But two men walked far from the sounds of revelry, far from the hot, exciting thud of Arioi drums and the stamp of dancing feet. Northward they strode in the gathering night by the side of the sea to a lonely and deserted place where a barren, rocky point thrust into tall black waves which rode in ceaselessly, endlessly from the undiscovered rim of the world.

"It is here?" Hoa Pahi asked.

Rata pointed to the vaulted, moonless sky. "The shadow of Oro was there—there where now you see the stars of Maui's bow. I cried aloud; I asked for strength and it has been given me. Now, Hoa Pahi, you will tell me why my prayer was answered, why I find myself unlike other men. You will tell me for what purpose I possess this power, and in what manner I shall make use of it. How did my father die?"

They had seated themselves on two smooth-worn boulders. The breath of the sea came cold against their cheeks, the sound of it filled their ears and, as when Rata had come alone before, the ground shuddered, spindrift fell like gusts of rain.

For long minutes Hoa Pahi did not reply and at last Rata bent near the older man. "Come, friend, the day has passed and I am king in my father's stead. Now you may speak aloud. Give voice to the scenes and sorrows which haunt your mind, and perhaps in the telling your heart will be eased, the sadness lessened. Let me know of Tumu-nui's death, for I shall avenge him if it take the rest of my years."

The helmsman passed a hand over his face, wiping the salt scud from his shaggy brows. His head remained averted and he stared out into the blackness with eyes clouded by the same dark shadows which Rata had often seen to lurk there since his return. "My son," he said, his words falling slowly, heavily, "are you still so young you have not learned that at times the gods make mock of us? Oro has in truth given

you superhuman strength. Have you thought that it may be only to lure you to the same end which met all those brave men with whom I sailed? There are things in this world which we cannot combat. Why do they exist? Why should monsters lie across the paths of men, waiting to crush their bones and to devour them? I do not know; unless it be to amuse the gods. Perhaps it is their laughter pealing which we hear when thunder crashes in the sky."

"Enough, Hoa Pahi!" said Rata sharply. "Enough of this mournful talk. Ask me no riddles of the way of the gods. Is it for us to read their minds or to question why the world is what we find it? If so, then should we ourselves be gods. No, Hoa Pahi, you have dwelt too long on the disasters you have seen and your thoughts have sickened. Too long you have lain idle, too long you have felt no bounding tiller in your hands. We cannot solve the mysteries that hem us on all sides, for we are only men. But as men we can live and fight and even die, if need be. We can act, and so we shall. In action your mind will heal even as Turia's and my mother's hands have healed your body. Show me the foe and we shall put to sea!"

In the dark Hoa Pahi smiled grimly. If, in duty bound, he had felt obliged to attempt discouragement of his young king, he realized now that it was impossible. Grim was the smile, for none knew as he that a new expedition, though headed by Rata himself, might well—yes, most probably would—disappear even as the last. Yet the smile came from the bottom of his heart. How he had longed during all the weeks of convalescence for the day when his feet might again be planted on the heaving steering platform of a war canoe, a ship following the course of Tumu-nui's own into the jaws of danger. Now he knew that it was to be, and his blood hurried in his veins as if he were again a youth of twenty. He put out a hand and seized Rata's wrist in an iron grip.

"It shall be as you wish. You shall have the story of how your father and his companions lost their lives. Then, though it be but to join them where they lie amid the rotting timbers of their ships, we shall follow. I shall show you the foe; a foe more terrible, more powerful and malignant than any your wildest dreams have conjured. Listen then.

"You remember the fair skies beneath which we left Tahiti. Once we were clear of the island's lee, a brisk and steady wind bellied our sails, the paddles were shipped, the bow waves curled away from the trim hulls. By evening Orofena and the lesser mountains we had left behind were far down on the horizon. Ah, but our hearts were high! Each man looked forward to the adventurous days ahead; each man felt equal to whatever might be in store. Every one of us, I believe, felt himself master of his fate—a brash and foolhardy frame of mind for mere mortals to indulge. Yet what voyage ever had more auspicious beginning? All the tapus had been observed, the gods had received the sacrifices due them, the priests had read the entrails of pigs slaughtered on the altars.

"And what did it all portend? Fair sailing! No wonder, then, that every paddleman's and warrior's spirit soared, no wonder that they sang and laughed as they stood their posts. So it continued for many a day. So, with bitterest irony, it continued to the *last* day.

"When the sun rose for the twentieth time we saw before us the single peak of the island where your father's sister reigns, and by nightfall the ships had been drawn ashore in a rocky cove. It is a pleasant land, both green and fertile, and there we were made most welcome so that the time went quickly. Many months had passed when at last Tumu-nui, drawn by his longing for your mother, ordered our departure.

"If our mood was buoyant upon leaving Tahiti, now was it doubly so as we set our course for home. Even the ships beneath us seemed possessed of an eagerness almost human. The sails tugged at the masts as, with creaking tackle and spray-wet decks, we pushed aside the sparkling seas, each rise and fall of the bows bringing us nearer the beloved shore.

"Then came a dawn of sullen gray. The wind died and beneath the glowering, solid-massed clouds the men picked up their paddles. No fish broke the oily surface of the ocean, no sea bird gave its raucous cry, nowhere as far as we could see was there sign of a living thing and a silence hovered in the skies, expectant and menacing, pressing like a heavy weight upon our entire company. Ah, if we had then turned back! If we had borne south or east or west! Yet we kept on, the prows pointing stubbornly, hopefully for home. Danger we might well have expected, for we then lay within the Paumotus, the Many Atolls—those low crouching circlets of coral flung like numerous seed over a thousand miles of sea. There they lie among twisting currents, waiting to grind to pulp the ships of unwary mariners. Dangers, yes; but such that men of courage and skill may outwit and conquer. If no worse had beset us, then might the generous Tumu-nui and all his men still be with us on this fair island, then might each one have returned to family and friends. But the horror lay ahead, disguised and unguessed. Both your father and I had looked upon it, yet were we unwarned.

"Standing above the others by the helm we could descry the feathered palm-tips which marked two atolls. They were strange to us; never had we passed that way before. Strange, too, was the island which lay between them. Island, I say, for the ground rose several hundred feet

71

above the doldrum ocean through which we made our sluggish way. Or was it ground? More like rock it seemed: a vast, unbroken rock stretching from atoll to atoll, gray-brown in color, scored by countless circling ridges. From broad, rounded summit it sloped away evenly to end in symmetrically widening, stone-smooth valleys at the shore line.

"Do you sense death and ruin in what I tell? Perhaps not; for I cannot myself explain the feeling which seized me as I gazed at that lumpish and apparently inanimate mass which squatted upon the bleak horizon. Through the torpid air I felt the breath of evil upon my face, the stench of a submarine creature exposed to light burned in my nostrils and my spine crawled with the conviction that we were watched, yet watched by what gloating, preying thing I could not say. Aboard all three vessels the crews had frozen motionless with paddles half upraised, and we floated aimless, like waiting statues on the somber plain. Yes, we waited while even the stoutest hearts halted—waited for the *unknown*.

"King Tumu-nui frowned as, with a hand shading his eyes, he scanned the two atolls and the great mound wedged between. Then he turned to me. 'Bring your ship about, Hoa Pahi,' he commanded.

"With an effort I broke the paralysis in which we all were held. I put pressure on the helm and shouted to the two rows of inert paddlemen. 'Back water on the starboard—forward to port!' Even as I spoke the words were sucked from my mouth and carried away. Suddenly the air all about us was in motion. With a dismal moaning it rushed toward the vast gray shape lying where met the sky and sea. The sails slatted wildly, then filled with a thunderous report and, raising the war canoes high in the water, wrenched them forward in a turbulent whirl of foam. There was utter confusion on each craft. Men were thrown to the decks, others struggled vainly to lower the tough matting triangles gripped by the wind. It was a futile effort. The next instant shrouds and lines snapped, the sails tore loose and streamed out before us like frantic, tattered banners. The rowers strained back on their paddles and I threw every ounce of my weight upon the helm. It was useless. We could as well have turned the ship had we ridden a mountain cataract, for now the entire sea was up-tilted and, seething and boiling, tumbled downwards to the menacing island. Island? Would to Oro it had been but a rocky shore on which we were to be dashed! At last we saw the awful, the incredible truth. The whole upper surface of that mountainous form was moving, was rising as if on a great hinge, was exposing a monstrous cavern which yawned wider and wider, drawing to its hungry maw air and sea and the puny men in wooden canoes who were caught between.

" 'Te Pahua, te Pahua!—The tridacna! The giant clam which lies athwart the seas to feed on men and ships!' Faint were the cries of the doomed men amid the tumult; faint and then stilled altogether as they stared fascinated at the terrible end to which they raced like twirling chips on a flood.

"The upper valve loomed higher and higher while the lower sank deeper and deeper in the leaden depths of the ocean. Our two escort vessels, lighter than the flagship, were drawn ahead. They passed within the frightful gaping jaws and the clam began to close—not swiftly like the tridacnas you have seen waiting silent in a dim lagoon to snap vise-like on the leg of a heedless diver, but with the slow, inexorable deliberateness with which the sun sinks to its rest or with which the stars wheel above. The lid of the sky was being clamped shut, eternal darkness was falling.

"But though all the gods and all nature then seemed to cry for his death, King Tumu-nui would not submit. To the last he fought, for himself and for those who served him. With the spear in hand which Tahua had given him at his coronation, he leaped from the steering platform and forced his way into the very bows. There he stood high above us all, and there, as he passed beneath the lowering, stone-cold lips, he struck a mighty blow . . ." Hoa Pahi's voice faded away and for some time the two men sat silent in the chill, wet night by the pounding sea.

When Rata spoke, he said briefly, tonelessly, "My father's spear was shattered."

"Yes."

"I know; I have seen. And how is it, Friend-of-the-Ship, that you are now here at my side?"

"Through a miracle, no less. Tumu-nui had no sooner dealt his final thrust at fate than the serrate jaws locked shut before my face. They ground through the ship just forward of my post as if biting through dried leaves, and suddenly, still grasping the tiller, I was spewed out like a bit of flotsam into the sea. Who shall say why I was spared? Was it the caprice of the powers that rule the world, was it

73

mere chance or accident? I cannot tell; yet often did I wish during the thirst-wracked, drifting days which followed that I had joined my king in his awful grave."

Rata rose to his feet. Then he bent and taking Hoa Pahi by both his hands drew him up beside him. "Who can say why you were saved? That can I. It was because I need you more than any other man. You were spared to pilot the greatest canoe that Tahiti has ever seen. So shall we build! You still draw breath to wield once more the rudder. You alone have lived that you may guide me, for my father's bones shall rest again in the land where he was born."

Hoa Pahi had no need to speak. The pressure of his handclasp told the tall young monarch all he had need to know. Together they turned and started back toward the far-off glow of the village fires.

XII

"PEOPLE OF TAHITI," said Rata, "you have heard from Hoa Pahi how our loved ones died, helpless against too great odds, yet unflinching to the end." It was some days after the coronation and again the village was crowded with those who had come at the command of the king. They filled the clearing about the royal residence, overflowed into the surrounding streets and even onto the near-by hillsides. Quietly they had listened to Hoa Pahi's account of the disaster. For months they had been aware of their loss and ignorant only of the manner in which it had come about. There is a limit to human grief and sorrow; the tears were already shed for the brave men gone forever, and now the only emotion of the crowd was one of dull anger—anger that such a thing should be, that the dread Pahua still spread himself between the atolls unscathed, unmolested and triumphant in evil victory.

"You have heard," Rata went on, "of Tumu-nui's last battle. It was your right to know, your right to glory in his defiance and his courage. Yet I have not summoned you but to listen to a tale of valor and then to return quietly to your homes, your comforts and pleasures. I have ordered this assembly to put to you an earnest question." He paused and there was an expectant hush throughout the village. Even the children who straddled the peaked roofs, the better to see, were silent and round-eyed, their play and laughter forgotten.

"Tahitians!" Rata cried and his voice carried to the most distant man. "Is this hateful deed to go unpunished? Shall our kinsmen lie forever within the hideous belly of Pahua? Are they to go unavenged?"

The pent-up ire of the people burst forth like a torrent which crashes through a clogging dam. "No!" rose up the deafening shout. "No, no! Death to Pahua! Death to the destroyer of our countrymen!"

Rata held up both his hands, but it was some time before he could speak again. The crowd milled restlessly. With clenched fists upraised, they pressed close about the king. "Lead us!" they cried. "Lead us, Rata; show us the way and we will follow!"

"Your anger pleases me," he said when they had quieted. "Anger is good when it rises against injustice and oppression; it is the sign of a race still young at heart. Your eagerness to fight is sweet as the tiare blossom to my nostrils, for so long as a people looks after its own, so long will it remain both great and vigorous. Lead? Verily, that I shall! And there will be work for every hand. Warriors will go with us by the hundreds, but for each fighting man there must be many who toil and plan and contrive at home. If a first expedition fail, then must a second be dispatched; if the second return not, then must a third go forth. Should your king succumb, then must another spring up to take his place.

"Listen, then, Tahitians, for this is war! War not against the crafty pillagers of Vavau, not against a tribe or clan, but war against a *thing* —a fearful thing which threatens all peacefully voyaging men. First, all you builders of canoes! Return to your homes and bring here to my capital your stone axes and adzes, your gimlets of polished shell. Bring all the sacred tools of your trade, for tonight they must sleep upon the marae in order that they may absorb the ingenuity and power of the gods. In the morning you will awaken them in the sea, for so shall they be bright and sharp for the attack upon tough woods, the axes for hewing, the adzes for gouging, the gimlets for boring. Three canoes we will build, two of great size, the third of a grandeur never seen before. Send out your scouts to find timbers for the lesser vessels, but leave to me selection of proper trees for the flagship.

"Makers of spears!—of long spears and short spears, of fishbone-barbed and sharktooth-studded spears; makers of pearl-shell hatchets, of slings, of sennit helmets and sennit armor, of all the weapons and accouterments of war. To work! Let no warrior of ours ever lack the means to deliver or to ward off a rain of blows.

"Weavers of rigging, of sails, of belts and clothing, let your fingers move nimbly. Whittlers of paddles, let the chips fly. Provisioners, gather food and drink, pig and fowl, fish and plant, for the artisans must not pause to hunt the wherewithal to fill their stomachs."

Rata's eyes roamed over his assembled subjects, and a thrill of pride ran through him. "These," he thought, "are the race of humans; they are my people. Pahua, or other insensate powers, may engulf them, but when the gods look down it cannot be with scorn. No, not with scorn, for a glowing, fighting spirit shines in their faces." Whether he or another led, they would keep on, no matter how great the danger, no matter how dark the shadows, and always for those who fell others would rise to fill the ranks. It was everlasting. Rata knew that he had but to beckon and any one of them would be at his side in the coming battle.

"Ehoma," he finished, trying to keep a huskiness from his voice, "Friends, need more be said? Each man knows his special skill and hence his duty. Let him do it, and a king can ask no more."

Thus Rata spoke on that day. The people listened to him, and then went with a will and did as he commanded. In the evening, the canoe-builders gathered at the marae. Silently they placed their tools in crevices of the holy structure, and then departed for the night. But with morning they were back. They seized the polished instruments and carried them to the shore. One after another they plunged the tools within the sea. "Awaken, axes!" they chanted, swinging the sharp stone blades in the brine. "Awake to fight and to attack! Awake for Tane, great god of artisans; awake for Taere, god of skills; awake for Te-fatu, god of armies. Awaken for Oro, god of war!" This done, they set off immediately in search of timber. Similarly in all other parts of the island the work of preparation began. And so it went on day after day without stint till a week had passed, then two, then three.

The escort vessels had taken final shape. The masts were being stepped, the last planks of the hulls were being fixed in place, bound fast with toughest sennit. Builders, both those within the ships and those without, sang as they passed the coconut fiber cord back and forth through the carefully drilled holes. "Thread it from outside, from inside, tie it fast! This is thy sennit, O Tane, to bind thy canoe! Let it ride short waves and long waves on near seas and far. This is thy sennit, O Tane—let it hold, let it hold!" They sang as they worked by the shore, for a song gives wings to even the most laborious task. Yet the hearts of the artisans were not light. For days their worry and apprehension had increased, though none had dared give it voice. But now at last one who had been calking tight the seams with breadfruit gum laid down his shell implement. He glanced up at the sun, which was no more than halfway up the morning sky.

"Brothers!" he said. The singing stopped and the workers' tools were held suspended. "What is to be done? If we continue, these canoes, the children of our hands, will be ready for launching before two days have passed. Could any augury be worse than that these humbler vessels should drink water before the king's own? Yet not so much as the keel of the flagship has been laid!"

"Peace, man!" said the chief architect, an elderly man with graying hair whose name was Hotu. "Put your mind to the work before you and tax it not with questions which are no concern of yours."

"But has not Rata insisted that all three ships shall slide down the sands to the sea together?" the other asked.

"Yes," the old man admitted with a frown, "that he has."

"Is he not at this minute still searching the forests with Hoa Pahi for the timber with which to build? Surely he has examined every tree that grows upon Tahiti, and none is straight enough or thick enough or tall enough to please him. Are we then to build to his design, which is of a length and breadth unheard of, in two days and two nights? Is the work of a month and more to be compressed into so short a time? It is madness, I say!"

"And you have said enough," Hotu replied sternly. "If all of us but sat giving vent to idle words then would not so much as one canoe be done." He turned upon his heel and walked away, but as he went he shook his head gloomily from side to side.

Nor were the canoe-builders alone in their concern. It spread throughout the island. There was questioning in all the scattered villages. "Have you heard?" they asked each other. "Those who have gone to see say that the ground where Rata's ship should stand is bare while our king wanders through the hills and forests, passing trunk after trunk of sound and sturdy timber, seeking always some fabulous tree whose upper branches scrape the sky."

"Yes," another would reply, "our Rata is great in stature, the greatest in all the world. But can it be that his mind has become addled and bewitched?"

While such words passed from mouth to mouth, Rata had in truth been searching. With his great axe of black and hard volcanic rock bound by a strip of purau bark to the flat of his back, he had tramped the forests where men habitually found the timber for their ships. It was true, as well, that he had been dissatisfied with all he saw. Through the long days Hoa Pahi had marched uncomplaining at his king's side, trying to keep pace with his short, stocky legs to Rata's long stride.

Yet now even the helmsman felt a secret discouragement. They stood upon a crest of the highest hills where nothing rose above save the mountains proper, and they gazed down on the wooded slopes of the valleys which fanned out to the sea below.

"There is no canyon, no ravine, no forest through which we have not walked," said Hoa Pahi. "You are right, Rata, when you say that your canoe must be more fleet, more strong and rugged than any Tahiti has produced. That is so, for the task ahead is greater than any ever undertaken. But we must make use of what the gods have given us. You have seen all that lies at man's hand with which to build."

Rata seemed lost in thought as with somber eyes he surveyed his native land spread out before him. Much indeed lay there, as Hoa Pahi expressed it, "at man's hand." Wherever he looked the earth was heavy with food-laden plants. Green groves of banana, thick with ripening fruit, crowded the tall sun-seeking breadfruit, the dark spreading mango, the stately chestnut-loaded mape. Huge blue-green leaves of taro filled the marshes, bamboo thicket and cane hugged the winding streams, fara and coconut bent over the lagoons. Rich, rich was Rata's kingdom, but he turned away, looked upward. Beyond lay a region where men seldom trod; beyond lay clouds and mystery, mountain gods and elves—and perhaps the forest giant which he sought.

"I think you are wrong," he said. "We have not seen all."

"Stay!" Hoa Pahi exclaimed, following the king's glance and reading as well his thought. "Would you tear the material for your ship from tapu ground? Take heed, Rata, and bring not still more dangers upon us."

"Peril there may be," Rata admitted, "but we must accept it in order to prevail over Pahua, which is the greatest peril of all. Come!" Swiftly he began the ascent toward Orofena, and Hoa Pahi, though with deep misgivings, followed.

Their way led first across a wide upslanting plateau, barren save for a coarse, tough grass which dragged at their ankles. The wind, as they went, grew ever stronger and more cool; yet the sweat streamed down Hoa Pahi's broad back, and when at last they reached the base of the mountain he threw himself down.

"Rata," he gasped, "you will have to match your steps to mine if you wish my company much farther."

"Why," Rata exclaimed, "we have only begun! The real struggle lies ahead."

"That I well believe," the seaman replied, "and I am only telling you that my legs, though serviceable enough aboard ship, were never meant to straddle mountains."

"There you say a true thing," Rata laughed. "All your strength lies in your arms, against which I would not match my own. But your legs, Hoa Pahi, are like an abbreviated afterthought, and I think it must have been intended that you move about the world in one way only: aboard a war canoe."

"That would suit me well enough," the helmsman admitted ruefully.

Rata seated himself beside the other. "Catch your breath. The day is still long before us and I feel, as I have not before, that success is near."

So they rested briefly and once more looked down on the coast land from which they had come. Rata's village lay almost directly at their feet, the houses shrunken to the size of birds' nests, the archers' field to a strip no larger than an outflung pareu; even the majestic pyramid of the marae rising from its long rectangular base seemed no more than a small mound of grayish sand and the heavy slabs which formed it no more than individual grains.

"We have come far," Hoa Pahi said when his breathing was easier, "far from the haunts of men." His voice was slightly hushed as though he felt a listening presence behind them. And such indeed the dark, towering mountain seemed.

Rata himself was not unaware of it as he answered quietly, "Yes, we near the spirit world, but we must not falter. Are you ready?"

Grunting, Hoa Pahi got to his feet, and Rata led on, but more slowly as the going became increasingly rough. Steeper and still more steep became the rock-strewn paths, till at last they were climbing vine-covered cliffs and precipices where they progressed more with hands and arms than legs, dragging themselves up by tough creepers, by dwarfed, spiny shrubs and by jutting ledges which often crumbled in their grasps. Yet the doughty mariner, with lips determinedly compressed, kept pace with his king, pulling himself ever higher by whatever came to hand, seizing upon the growing vines as though he hauled upon rough sennit lines to hoist a sail or raise an anchor. Here and there they passed solitary trees, and some were of noble stature, but Rata never paused. Higher, higher they fought their way, through rocky flumes and chimneys, up sheer and slippery clefts, ever up and up. The air became thin and cold and Orofena's cloud cap hid the sun. Sudden rains attacked them on the buffeting wind, blinding and almost suffocating them in drenching downpours, then passing on as quickly to leave them dazed, clinging to the almost perpendicular mountain wall where white-flashing cataracts, newly sprung to life, rushed noisily seaward on either side.

Only once Rata looked back at Hoa Pahi, who crowded upon his heels. "Keep on, Friend-of-the-Ship!" he smiled. "The port we seek is near."

"And so it must be," said Hoa Pahi grimly, "unless it lies within the clouds themselves." Then, as Rata did not move, he looked above and saw the reason why. The face of the cliff swerved outward, forming a smooth and stony roof above their heads. It was bare of any growing thing, bald as a turtle's egg. Not even within the long reach of Tahiti's

81

king was there handhold however small. To have gone farther on that path could have had but one result: two bodies would have gone hurtling through the air to the rocks a thousand feet below.

XIII

I T IS CLEAR," said Hoa Pahi soberly, "that human beings were never meant to see what lies beyond."

"That I do not believe," Rata replied. "Often the gods present us with a blank wall which it appears no man can hope to pierce. But we are given heads upon our shoulders with brains within and my mind tells me that to stare at this obstacle, to dwell upon it, bemoan or curse it will not remove it. Let us rather ignore it and look away; perhaps another path lies open." Slowly he began to inch his way to the right, gripping with his bare toes, with his nails and hands each smallest niche or stub projection which the rock afforded. He had gone a distance of some twenty feet when the steersman, who had watched with anxiety his king's creeping progress, gave a sudden shout.

"Rata!" he called, "Rata!" He looked above and he looked below. The younger man had disappeared as though swallowed by the mountain. But a voice was to be heard and it had a strangely hollow ring.

"Follow me, Hoa Pahi; follow me, for already I see our journey's end."

Hoa Pahi did as he was bidden, and he was still cautiously and intently choosing his way when Rata's arm whipped out, seized him by the wrist and drew him up into the mouth of a roughly circular tunnel which opened directly upon the sheer rock wall. It sloped upward steeply, yet compared with the precipitous crags they had already scaled it was an easy climb. At a distance equal to three war canoes laid end to end, the tunnel opened on the light of day. Scudding clouds were framed by the irregular orifice, and squarely in the middle rose the arrow-straight shaft of a mighty tree.

Rata asked, "Have we not triumphed over Orofena?"

But Hoa Pahi's astonishment was such that he could make no

reply. He could only follow once more, to the best of his ability, the other's now recklessly hurrying ascent till he emerged again in the open air. There, side by side, they remained for long moments gazing before them in unbelief.

Clutched in the guardian grip of the highest peaks, like a green pearl held skyward in offering of unmatched beauty to the hosts above, lay a densely wooded valley, more lush, more verdant than any their eyes had ever beheld. Grass carpeted all the ground, ferns grew to the size of Hoa Pahi, flowering shrubs as tall as Rata. The forest trees stabbed the heavens with a stature that must have equaled the gods themselves. Yet one tree pushed its way above all others. It stood in the exact center of the grove and its many brothers, ranged about, seemed placed there—great as they were—but to do it humble homage. The massive roots sank through the rich loam to clutch solidly the vitals of the mountain; the tremendous trunk shot from its heavily buttressed base to mount upward in majestic, sweeping flight till it was lost completely in the clouds.

"A Moi!" Rata breathed exultantly. "A king-tree!"

"Yes," Hoa Pahi's voice mirrored his wonder, "a king-tree of Ihu-ata, god of cliffs and crags and pinnacles." He glanced at the other, and noted with alarm the rapt expression upon his face. "Think not, Rata," he said hurriedly, "to put your axe to that tapu trunk!"

"A Moi!" Rata murmured to himself as if he had not heard. "A king-tree for my canoe." And he moved forward into the mystic valley.

There are places on this earth which by their very nature are sacred to the gods and the spirits of the air. They are places of exceeding beauty and far remote, of a pristine purity, yet so freshly green that they might have sprung from creation but yesterday. They hold a fragile silence, but it is a silence which seems filled with soft, elusive whisperings. Nothing stirs, but if a human stumble upon such an enchanted spot he senses vague movement all about. What brushes softly against his hand, his cheek? Is it a breath of air, a caress—a warning? What are the countless beings which he *feels* but cannot see?

Such was the green-clad mountain cleft into which the two men of Tahiti stepped, Hoa Pahi with cushioned, reverent tread and Rata as though sleepwalking, spellbound by the grandeur of the lordly Moi, from which he never took his eyes. At the distant end of the glade a river spilled through a narrow sluice high on the mountainside to fling itself cascading white into space, then down to some hidden mossy basin far below. No sound of the tumbling, foaming waters reached the intruders, but veils of fine mist parted from the air-borne stream to drift slowly toward them in successive pearly, vaporous curtains mingling with the occasional whorls of cloud-stuff which dipped down from the sky, filling the valley with beautiful and bewildering shifting lights. Momentarily one saw clearly. Then vision was obscured, confused by the opalescent haze. Perpetual dew clung to perfumed petals, to grasses and thick foliage. It was a fairyland in which a man was tempted to rest beneath a flower-dusted tamanu, silent and motionless, in the hope of surprising some elfin creature in his gambols through the shading leaves.

But Rata was of a single purpose. He strode into the forest and straight to the base of the Moi. He wrenched off the purau cord with which his axe was bound against him and he seized the handle.

"Think twice of what you do!" Hoa Pahi warned again. "Will you risk the anger of Ihu-ata?"

"To avenge my father I will risk anything," he replied, and swung the heavy stone blade with all his might so that the echo of the blow bounded back and forth from peak to peak. Was there not also a sound as of innumerable suddenly intaken, horrified breaths? Hoa Pahi thought so, but Rata never paused. His axe rose and fell. The chips flew. Soon great chunks of wood strewed the ground about them. Great was Rata's strength, but great also was that of the sacred tree which for years by the hundred had grown unmolested within the undiscovered glen. Hours passed, and still it refused to bow to the lowland king. But as sundown neared and the light began to fade, there came a groaning and snapping from the deeply gashed trunk. Rata and Hoa Pahi stepped back. They looked aloft. Through a rift in the clouds they could see the highest branches and the final spear-point top of the doomed Moi. To them it seemed as if a struggle went on at the apex of the regal column, as if the living tree were possessed of a will of its own, a will to keep its lofty head far above all Tahiti, its face turned to the skies. The summit trembled and swayed. Yet for minutes Ihu-ata's pillar refused to bend. Rata was about to lift his axe once more when a shudder passed through the stubborn trunk, the last remaining thin support splintered and the king-tree dipped earthwards. But even in its fall there was a slow majesty befitting the Moi of a lonely forest. It bowed to fate with leisured and unhurried dignity; only in the last moment did it speed its descent and then it was in a mighty rush of anger. With deafening crash it smote the ground, and the sound and shock of it traveled to bring fear and alarm in every seashore village.

Both Rata and his helmsman stared in awe at the prostrate giant. Standing upright it had seemed immense; strangely, lying there in defeat, it appeared greater still. Involuntarily and in unison their eyes swerved to the gaping space the tree had filled. What did they expect to see? Ihu-ata in tangible, perceptible shape? Perhaps. But there was nothing. If before they had imagined the valley to stir with invisible life, now, so they felt, the darkening place was utterly deserted, completely empty.

"Let us return to our homes," said Hoa Pahi, unable to repress a slight shiver.

"Yes." Rata picked up the cord and bound his axe about him. "We may go; it is done."

"It is," the other agreed with no enthusiasm.

"What I have brought to pass," Rata replied, quickly guessing his thought, "was for a reason upon which not even the gods could frown."

"Can we then read the mind of Ihu-ata?"

"We cannot, Hoa Pahi. We can only act according to our light."

Silently they made their way to the tunnel and began the arduous descent. It was not till hours later when they were entering the village in the light of a full moon that Hoa Pahi spoke again.

"I cannot help wondering, Rata, why you have told the people that our fleet will be launched by the day after tomorrow. It is not wise to disappoint them, and all will think it a bad omen for a desperate venture." Rata did not reply immediately and he added, "To hew timbers from the Moi and get them to the shore is a labor of weeks in itself."

"I cannot answer your question," Rata said at length. "I do not know why I spoke as I did nor why I have continued to insist that we shall put to sea on the day fixed. Have you never noticed that there are times when the words our lips form seem not our own? So it has been with me. Something outside of and beyond myself has spoken those words, and I have felt them true. I *still* feel them to be true. Tomorrow I shall bring a hundred workmen to the mountain. And on the day following, Friend-of-the-Ship, we shall sail!"

Hoa Pahi shook his head in the darkness, but he said nothing to mar the youthful confidence of the king, and so they parted, Hoa Pahi to go to his sleeping mat, and Rata to stalk restlessly the silent and deserted streets of his capital. The canoe builders, the spear and paddle makers, the fishermen, the women and children—all rested on the cool woven fara leaves folded in a peaceful sleep. So it was all round the curving shores of the calm lagoons, and so it must also be, Rata imagined, throughout all the island of Tahiti.

He was tremendously mistaken.

In that high-flung valley hanging close beneath the moon there was a very different scene. There, far from heavy-headed men and dull mortality, sleep had no existence. There the luminous night was filled with delicate, fragile life, teemed with a horde of tiny beings. Elves! The elves of Ihu-ata, sprung by the thousands from the low-bending, huge-leaved plants, from the rocks, the cliffs, the shimmering silvered air! They glided down the darkly glinting waterfall, rode out into the valley clinging to the moonbeams and the diaphanous, palely phosphorescent veils of trailing mist. They passed over the dew-wet grass, over the wide-spread petals of fragrant, night-blooming flowers, to light in swarms about the dethroned Moi.

Shrill and high rose their treble bird voices.

"Ah!" exclaimed their chief, whose name was Tuoi-papa-papa, "this is the work of Rata, that king who fears neither god nor man. It must be rectified!" Tuoi-papa-papa was a very handsome elf. As chief he was, as is proper whether among humans or others, taller than his fellows. His height was fully six inches and his little body was molded with a beauty no less than Rata's own. There was, in fact, a remarkably strong resemblance between the chief of the elves and the king of Tahiti, so that in looking at Tuoi one might easily have thought it was Rata seen at a great distance.

Now a short-bodied and very homely mite of an elf spoke up. It was Fefera, who stood in relation to Tuoi much as did Hoa Pahi to Rata. "Tuoi-papa-papa," he said, "this must indeed be corrected, and I have to smile when I think of the surprise of that lowland ruler when he returns tomorrow." Smile he did, even as he had proclaimed himself obliged; his miniature, squarish mouth expanded so that it covered his entire face—and he was the image of Hoa Pahi.

The chief, too, smiled a little. "Yes," he agreed, "the great blundering creature will not believe his eyes." Tuoi then cupped diminutive, flower-like hands to his mouth and piped, "O elves! Come by the thousands and let us raise this Moi which is stricken, chopped down by Rata!"

XIV

NO ONE will deny the wonder of the magic wrought that night on Orofena's concave crest. Yet while the elves of Ihuata toiled busily above, another miracle—no less great, although more oft repeated—happened down below.

Rata was perplexed by his unwonted sleeplessness. Perhaps, he told himself, it is the exceeding brilliance of the moon; or, possibly, a mounting exhilaration brought on by successful conquest of the Moi. He did not know, and his feet roamed restlessly the now cool grasses in the hushed lanes of the village. Once he stopped abruptly when a distant sound reached his ears. He looked to the tiered mountains rising one upon another, dim bulwarks of Orofena. The highest sky-borne peak from which the souls of the dead take final flight swam free and clear in the illumined heavens, and for long moments he remained, staring, listening for a repetition of a sound such as the Moi's boughs had made when they whipped through the thin upland air. It did not come again, and he started on once more.

"Go to your home," he thought impatiently. "Stretch upon the mat and close your eyes." But still he continued, half annoyed by the aimlessness of his wanderings and at the same time unable to bring them to an end. He was vaguely reminded of his ocean-walking dream. Was there not something strangely similar in this pointless stroll? Again he had the sense of groping for an unknown thing. But there seemed a difference, too. Before, his *mind* had been hunting, seeking, striving to find a friend who was lost. And now? He shook his head, conscious only of an unaccustomed kindling of his blood, of a stirring attuned in some mysterious way to the murmurous, heavily perfumed tropic night. "Old-woman-of-the-sea," he smiled, "you should be here to point out my path. Which way is a man to turn?"

Well might Rata have added, when he explained to Hoa Pahi that a mortal's words not always are his own, that the same holds most true of actions. Suddenly, he left the slumbering settlement and, no longer indecisive, made for the near-by coast. Arrived at the shore, he turned without hesitation southward and followed the curving line of the bay as far as a narrow point which stood forth to shield the region just beyond from currents, storms and trades. Here, as if in answer to a guiding inner compulsion, he struck off inland across the little peninsula, weaving between the leaning boles of coco palms, brushing aside scattered clumps of somnolently drooping elephant-ear or sweet-scented tiare, moving always at steady pace as does a man who goes to an appointed meeting. And to a meeting Rata went in fact, although to one not of his own devising. Rather was it a joining long, long prearranged—appointed by the same whimsical gods who determined the nature of mankind even as they determined the shape and position of the islands in the southern seas.

He stepped forth onto the border of the sheltered cove where since boyhood he had beached his small canoe, and only then, when he saw that Turia waited beneath the fara tree, he briefly paused.

She was distant less than half a javelin's throw, seated where the dark-glossed pandanus leaves cast bars of shadow on the strand, motionless as the fara's sinuous, naked arms which twined jet black across the moonlit sky. *Vahine-Tahiti*. She might have been the first and last, the only woman of the islands—a creature spawned by the fertile seed-filled earth and the drowsing, languorous lagoon, by the wild exuberant, almost audibly upthrusting jungles and the warm, caressing air.

To Rata, beholding her, there came gradually dawning understanding of the hurrying fire in his blood, of the meaning of his movements; even, perhaps, of the meaning of his life. Now his eyes could see! —and he wondered, fleetingly, if it was no more than slow, unnoticed passing time which so abruptly cleared the sight, which so transformed a merely fond companion to show him the mating part of his own self, the focus of desire. But what matter when the wonderwork has come to pass! He went forward quickly to her side.

"Come," she said softly, "Amai na," and raised her arms to him. A large flower burned whitely in the dark cloud of her hair, wreathed oval-petaled tiare fell from about her throat to lie lightly on the sheer tapa at her breasts. "Amai na," she repeated—"come near to me."

He took the outstretched hands and at their touch a tremor passed through his frame. "Turia!" He said her name again; and then again, slowly, lingeringly. What fresh delight in the familiar syllables!

"Yes," she replied, "Turia—nothing more."

"No," he said. "Ah, no." For once this girl with the deeply percep-
tive eyes was wrong. "It is more, much more. You are here; I am here.
But there is also the great enchantment. Do you not feel it wrapped
about us?"

She nodded, drawing him down beside her. "Aué, Rata," she sighed,
breathing her happiness into the word of many moods, "Aué, it is good."

Still holding her hands in his, he let his glance sweep from one end
of the cove's shallow crescent to the other, then out beyond, as if he
would assure himself of reality. But yes, this was his island firm beneath
him, his native soil. The slender, frond-covered shape at the base of the
tree was his canoe. The shimmering waters enclosed by the pale white
fire of reef-crumbled seas were those over which it had so often carried him.

It was all true, then. He turned back to her, bending close. And
this was his vahine. "Yes, Turia, the thing which quivers here between
us is wondrous good. Yet how strange that it should bring weakness
into the knees of Tahiti's strongest man, dizziness to his brain, hunger
to his loins, that it should bear him forward as the shell of a coconut is
whirled on a mountain stream!"

"By the same current," she murmured, "am I also drawn."

"But see what is done, Turia," he exclaimed in rapturous amazement. "Only see . . ."

What would you say, Rata? That all cares, all thoughts of death or
pain or sorrow retreat beyond the senses' small periphery? That the universe narrows, converging on—existing for—yourselves alone? Well,
trouble not; words are thrown away. It is not for you to consider that
the vital pulse rising in yourself and your beloved is that which has carried your race from its unknown cradle to strew them over all the Pacific
isles. Nor is it for you to ponder that in the same way are your people
launched in a future holding a single certainty: that they shall continue on. Leave such thoughts to the tellers of tales, the singers of songs,
who will follow after, and do you but give joyous birth to the miracle
which makes them true.

"Mea nehenehe," he whispered, gazing deep into the shadowed eyes.
"You, too, are beautiful."

Unnoticed, far away on Eimeo's blurred, ocean-merging shore,
moved a speck of flame where some solitary fisherman walked with his

rama of burning fronds held high. Unseen, a little owl alighted at the water's edge to inspect the shallows. Unheard, a flurry of minnows shattered, with a sound of sudden rain, the lagoon's dark mirror.

His hands passed over the soft-textured tapa and, closing her eyes, the girl lifted her face upward. She gave a shake to her head which sent the filmy tips of her hair brushing the sands behind. This Turia had done once before beneath the fara tree. Now, as then, she confronted—and accepted—the inevitable. But this was *glad* acceptance. Who would think to change the ways of the turning world? Who would wish to? It was meant to be so; marvelous land in which it was meant to be so! When his cheek touched hers she lay slowly back upon the powdered coral. Her arms folded about him and she breathed the scent of crushed tiare.

"Aué, Rata . . . Aué!"

XV

FOR SOME MOMENTS after he awakened on the next morning Rata lay unmoving, allowing his eyes to wander over the pleasingly precise pattern of the walls. Close beside him countless minute chinks in the plaited bamboo were bright with sunlight. At the far end of the dwelling the sleeping mats were rolled for the day, his mother and Turia already gone. Turia . . . His still languid thoughts drew her near again. What unguessed beauty was he not discovering—he who had imagined he knew all that Tahiti had to offer. But suddenly his eyes narrowed, his lips became firm. This was no time for day-dreaming, however delightful. There was work to do!

He sprang to his feet and drew deep draughts of the sweet, fresh air into his lungs; he stretched his long arms above his head, flexing the muscles, reveling in his own abundant strength. Soon he would have use for those muscles, use for every ounce of power which surged in his great body. The time of preparation, he thought, was nearly at an end. Up there on Orofena the Moi lay waiting for the adzes of his workmen; the long search was over and it remained only to form a royal war canoe from the splendid tree.

Down to the water's edge he ran and plunged into the sea, throwing himself this way and that like a playful porpoise, flinging the spray about, dashing the last vestige of sleep from his eyes. Then, wrapping a dry maro about his waist, he went briskly to the cookhouse, where he found his mother breakfasting, served by three young women.

The cookhouse of the royal family was little different from any other; there was a low-hanging roof of niau fronds, but it stood open on all sides. A fire burned in a circle of stones and the Queen was seated with simple dignity upon the clean white sand with which the floor was sprinkled. Rata stepped quickly to her, bent low to give a tender greeting, then took his place. A large round purau leaf on which were three

small, bright red fish and several steaming wild bananas was placed before him and he began to eat with appetite.

Queen Maemae watched him smiling. "Care rides your shoulders lightly on this morning," she observed after a time.

"Yes," he agreed happily, "I am quite filled with joy."

"And Turia as well."

He looked up abruptly with expression so startled that his mother laughed aloud. "You know?"

"Of course." She nodded contentedly. "Is not such a fine happening pleasure for all to share? By now the news has surely traveled as far as Turia's village if it has not already flown the channel to Eimeo. It is right that you have found your princess; all is as it should be. But we must bestir ourselves, for here again great preparation is required."

"Later," he said gently.

"Later . . . ?"

"When I have gone and then returned."

There was a silence before Queen Maemae replied. "Very well; perhaps it is better so. We shall wait, Turia and I." After a moment she asked, "Is there not also other cause of your high spirits?"

He tossed a fish head to the dogs circling outside the little hut. "Yes," he admitted, "there is another thing which has added to my happiness. I have found and felled the timber for my canoe. Did you not hear it fall?"

"A sound we heard, but it was more like the thunder of colliding clouds. Some, in their fright, exclaimed that it must have been a mountain which you, in anger at not finding what you sought, had toppled from its base. Do you tell me it was but a single tree which rocked the ground beneath our feet?"

"Mother mine," said Rata, "it was a Moi—a giant and a king."

"A Moi!" The Queen turned to her son with a frown upon her lovely face. "If you have in truth done such a thing, Rata, then temper your elation, postpone your rejoicing, for such sacrilege will not pass unnoticed."

"Yet pass it has. No hand rose to stay me and the tree lies outstretched like a whale cast on the reef." He raised his eyes and noticed that one of those who served his mother was the young girl who, on the day of Hoa Pahi's return, had thrown herself upon him in supplication for news of her beloved. Grief no longer marred her features, but she was quite unsmiling.

"Courage," he said impulsively. "Soon, soon your Rai and his comrades will be avenged!" Poor comfort, he thought; but she nodded slowly and although he saw no lessening of the sorrow in her eyes, he read there a boundless faith that what he said was true. "May it be so," he muttered under his breath, "may it be so!"

His mother placed a small hand upon his wrist. "Rata," she said seriously but with great tenderness, "do not raise their hopes too high. It would be no kindness . . ."

He stopped her with the warm pressure of his fingers over hers.

93

"We, too," he whispered, "must have high courage." Then he rose quickly, not to see the mist which swam before her eyes. He brushed aside the tips of the fronds at the eaves and stepped out.

"Hotu!" he called.

The gray-haired chief of the builders left the nearly completed canoes and hurried to him.

"Hotu," said Rata, "gather a hundred of your best men. We leave immediately for the mountains. Bid them bring their tools and a bit of food, for the path is long and hard and leads to the very summit of Orofena, where I have downed the finest timber it has ever been your fortune to work. In it your trained eye will see the most lordly vessel ever fashioned, and you shall bring it into being. Make haste now, haste!"

The architect went to carry out the king's command and in a short while returned followed by a hundred artisans, each bearing a basket slung from the shoulder in which were tools, a few mangos or roasted chestnuts or a slice of breadfruit. "We are ready," he reported.

Rata looked over the assembled company. These men, canoe-builders all, were respected in the community. Theirs was a craft of skill and one not learned in a day. From father to son that skill and the traditions of careful work and strong were handed down. The secrets of the trade were guarded with religious zeal as were the ceremonies of their separate marae. But much as Rata admired their ability, he, the natural warrior born, could not fail to see that there stood before him, not fighting men, but simple artisans, wielders of peacetime tools. They had neither the physique nor the bold eye of those for battle bred and trained. It may have been these considerations which caused him to sound a note of warning.

"Shipwrights! I have called you and you have come. But this is no ordinary task to which we march. We go to regions of which your ancestors lived and died in ignorance, to regions which they held in fear and awe. Yesterday I shattered a great tapu; I walked within a sacred grove and felled a sacred tree. You heard the angry, roaring fall and you felt the island tremble. That sound, that shudder of the earth was the Moi of Ihu-ata crashing to its end."

The chins of the workmen sagged and their eyes widened round. Consternation and dread were in their faces as they looked at one another. Here, surely, was proof of what they had long suspected. The

94

king was no longer sane; his soul had been devoured by an evil spirit which even now must crouch within his bowels. At what would a man stop who would walk within and desecrate a temple of the gods? Were they to be led but to become living sacrifices, long-fish, suspended about Ihu-ata's altars? Their fear-filled mutterings rose to the ears of the king and a frown darkened his features.

"What I have done, adzmen, hewers, caulkers and sennit-binders —what I have done and lived to tell of—you may also do. The fact that I stand before you should testify that you need not cringe. Not long ago you shouted a lusty 'No!' when I demanded whether Tumu-nui should lie forever within Pahua's slime. Do you falter now? Be bold! Bind tightly the maros with the sawtooth design which is all your own and do not forget that I, though but a man, may also be feared if moved to anger. Forward now, and fit your steps to mine."

Clearly the final admonition was to be taken in a figurative sense, for the workmen took three steps to Rata's one. But move forward they did, however sullenly and ill at ease, and it is possible that the king's ire seemed more immediate than whatever they might encounter in the distant cloudlands.

The procession had neared the village outskirts when Rata observed that Hoa Pahi strode stolidly at his side as he had done through all the recent weeks. He stopped abruptly and turned to that constant companion.

"Hold on, Hoa Pahi," said he. "For more than a score of days you have bruised your feet on the sharp rocks of these trails. Together we have accomplished what we set out to do. There is no need for you to come again. Remain at home and rest, for tomorrow your real work begins. Tomorrow those wide feet with spreading toes will grip smooth boards. You will be at the helm!"

"I am no man to count fish before they struggle on my spear," the other replied. "Still I pray it be as you say, for I long to have the smell of the sea in my nostrils."

"So you shall." Rata raised his arm to those behind, motioning them forward, and he set out from the village. And Hoa Pahi, quite regardless of the king's words, fell in a step behind. They were well into the hills when Rata, chancing to turn, again discovered him.

"What is this!" he exclaimed. "Did you not hear me say you might remain below?"

"I did," Hoa Pahi answered calmly, "but little rest I should have enjoyed for thinking of you once more bearding Ihu-ata. I prefer to keep you in my sight."

A great laugh of frank delight escaped the king. Wrapping both arms about his faithful henchman he drew him hard against his chest. "If I had a dozen like you I would have no fear of Pahua nor of all the gods of heaven. Have it as you will. I do not deny it pleases me to have one man who does not cower at the thought of ghosts and spirits." With a scornful glance at the carpenters who now straggled far behind he turned his face to the mountain. "Onward, Hoa Pahi!"

It was well after noon when the last of the canoe-builders reached the base of the tunnel-pierced cliff which led to the valley of the Mois. Here Rata and Hoa Pahi had waited and now again the king addressed them.

"We near our goal," he said, "but there is danger in the ascent ahead. Cut yourselves long vines and twine them together to make cords; grasp them between you so that if one slip others may stay his fall and hold him from death on the rocks below."

The artisans gazed apprehensively at the sheer wall with its outward-sloping brow; they stared down from the dizzying height to the safety of the lowlands and some, with heads suddenly reeling, sat quickly on the ground. Others shifted uneasily from foot to foot, and a handful went to do as Rata had instructed. Old Hotu, their chief, alone seemed undismayed and his shame for his men was plain to see. Rata spoke quietly in his ear.

"Follow after Hoa Pahi; I will come last lest there be some who at this point are minded to turn back." Then to the steersman: "Take them straight to the tree and let the first arrived set immediately to work."

With a nod Hoa Pahi assailed the cliff, Hotu close after.

"Come!" Rata shouted as the others hesitated. "Up with you!" and seizing the first of the chain of vine-bound men he lifted him bodily onto the precarious path. The rest began to move, and soon a slow centipede crawled along the face of the cliff, a centipede with unsteady legs and quaking knees.

When the last man had passed, Rata followed, fuming at the precious time which was slipping by. It seemed to him a full hour before he stepped again from the mouth of the tunnel into the eerie beauty of the valley. But instead of the sound of scores of axes hacking, trimming bark and branches, which he had expected, an utter silence met his ears, a silence as complete as that which he and Hoa Pahi had discovered when first they set eye upon the enchanted glade. The canoe-builders, all of them, huddled motionless in a frightened group but a few paces from the tunnel.

"How now!" Rata roared with a rush of anger. "Is this the manner in which you carry out my orders? Do you thus hurry the launching of my fleet? Do you cower here with the implements of your trade dangling idle in the baskets on your craven backs? I have watched you awaken your tools in the ocean; better had you immersed yourselves in the bracing sea, for you sleep upon your feet! To the tree, artisans—get you to the tree which I have leveled for your use!"

"O Rata," said Hotu in a voice that was none too steady, "we look upon this forbidden valley which we see, though mistily, from end to end. Many a Moi meets our eyes and one which seems the king of all. But all stand erect as they were made and none bows down to earth."

Rata noticed then that not even Hoa Pahi had gone into the grove but stood near by with an expression of incredulity and stupefaction on his weather-beaten face. The helmsman raised a blunt forefinger and silently pointed. Rata whirled and looked. Impossible! It could not be! Had all the events of yesterday been nothing more than a figment of his imagination? Had all his sweating labor with the axe been just another dream? He felt of the palms of his hands. No—those hardened calluses were real, and so was Hoa Pahi's dumfounded astonishment. Yet there stood the Moi in all its disdainful majesty, rising above the primeval forest with its highest branches once more brushing the sky, drinking the moisture of the clouds! For a long moment Rata remained as though turned to stone and no one spoke in the encompassing silence. To the fear-sharpened ears of the canoe-builders there came a sound, infinitely faint, as of tinkling, flute-like laughter. It may have been but the chirping of unseen birds, but they looked, cringing, into the empty air from which it seemed to issue. At last Rata broke the spell.

"Hoa Pahi," he said evenly, "you once told me that there are times when the gods do mock us. And so it is today. Our work is undone and the Moi towers once more unscarred in challenge. It is Ihu-ata's whim to toy with us." Rata's voice rose so that with head thrown back he appeared to address not the trembling artisans but the thrusting peaks surrounding them. "Let him not think so easily to discourage the king of Tahiti. He has raised the Moi in its place—and I shall cut it down again!"

Rata took the axe from his back and swung it in his hand. He turned to the workers of wood. "Rest and partake of the food you have brought," he directed, "for by sundown I shall be ready for you." Then with only Hoa Pahi beside him he marched again into the forest. Arrived at the base of the tree he gave not so much as an upward glance but drove again, with redoubled effort, his blade of stone into the living trunk. His blows had resounded but a short while when he became aware of Hotu standing near. The man's lined and aging face bore a look of worry and trepidation and it was apparent that he wished to speak.

"Yes, Hotu," said Rata, impatient of interruption, "what is it? Speak quickly, man, for time is short."

"It is an evil thing I have to say," the other replied haltingly.

"I am used to evil tidings; on a day when even the gods conspire against me one thing more can make no difference."

"I had never thought the time would come when I should lose pride in my profession and in those who share it." The chief architect's eyes were bent upon the ground at his feet. "That thing has happened. My men refuse to spend a night within this valley. Rather, they say, would they die a hundred deaths than flout the tapus of so sacred a place. They would return to their homes." Hotu ceased speaking and tears of humiliation started down his cheeks.

Rata rested the head of his axe upon the ground and leaned heavily upon the handle. A weariness suddenly assailed him. It was a weariness such as he had not felt since the night when he had stood beside the helm of his father's ship beneath the eaves of the palace while Hoa Pahi fought for life within. On that long-past night the sense of his loss, the loss of Tumu-nui, had momentarily weakened him; it had seemed he could not go on without his father's firm support. And now he was again deserted but in fashion still more bitter, for this was voluntary abandonment by his own people, and it came at the most crucial moment of Rata's life.

"So," he said slowly, "I am left alone. Am I then to build my great canoe with my own two hands?" His glance roved to Hoa Pahi, who remained with his feet planted wide apart, his brawny arms folded over his broad chest, unflinching, solid as a rock. Very gradually a smile spread over Rata's face, his grip tightened about the thick handle of the axe and he no longer leaned upon it. He felt his powers return and go bounding through his frame.

"No!" he exclaimed. "Not alone, Friend-of-the-Ship, for you stand by me! So be it. Go, Hotu, and lead your artisans to the snug safety of their thatch roofs. Yet tell them they need not fear the anger of their king, for I see I have been wrong. I had done better to bring a hundred warriors. More would they have accomplished with the points of spears than these men with all their useless sacred tools. But one cannot look for winged flight from the timid land-crab. Go, Hotu, though I know that if I asked it, you yourself would stay; leave me with my helmsman, for together we shall continue to do battle with the gods!"

Sorrowfully Hotu walked away. Soon the last of the workers had scuttled through the tunnel to disappear. Once again Rata and his friend were alone with the shrouded valley, its mystery and its waiting silence.

"Well, Hoa Pahi, what say you now?"

The mariner tilted back his head and squinted aloft, scanning the length of the defiant Moi as at sea he might look to the masthead to assure himself of the set of the sails.

"I say," he pronounced deliberately, "lay on!"

XVI

RATA attacked the king-tree with greater fury than before; but it was late afternoon when its grip was loosened from the sky and it crashed once more to measure its length on the valley floor. The sun had long since passed below the rim of the cup-shaped recess in which the two Tahitians stood, but its flaring, reddening rays reached into the heavens above them, painting vividly the under surface of the clouds and sending a reflected roseate light into the valley itself, so that the cliffs, the curling water-fall and the flimsy draperies of leisurely drifting mist were all touched with a faintly glowing, lambent fire. It was a soft, diffused illumination which seemed to draw out and heighten the color of every plant, moss and stone within Ihu-ata's sacred grove. The cool, moist grasses, the graceful feathery ferns, the glossy elephant-ear were green with a lucent greenness beside which their lowland brothers were dull and pale. The delicate blossoms with which the mape trees were powdered, the low-growing Tahitian gardenia, the jasmine clusters shone with a creamy whiteness that appeared to spring from some source of light within themselves.

"Little wonder," thought Rata, who rested, still breathing hard from his recent labor, while the beauty sank within him, "little wonder that men have discovered each growing thing, each mountain crag and rock, to be instinct with deity. On such an evening, in such a place, one can almost see their spirits stir in life, almost hear their whispered word."

He gazed down at the recumbent Moi. "You, too," he said aloud, "were a thing of beauty and of spirit. But it is not in wantonness I have brought you low. You will live again, and though in different form, it will be no less fair." Hoa Pahi stood near and Rata took his hand. "Come, stout warrior. We must prepare to cling to that which we have won. If Ihu-ata raises this tree again he shall take our bodies with it."

They walked along the trunk till they came to a spot where it bridged a slight depression in the ground. "This will do," Rata decided. "Get yourself under, Hoa Pahi." The helmsman crawled into the hollow, where he lay with the rough bark of the Moi just above, and Rata, with more difficulty, followed. They drew the evergreen branches close about them so that although it was possible to see without through the interstices of the foliage they were themselves completely hidden. "Make yourself comfortable," Rata advised, "for the wait may be long."

Hoa Pahi, hardy seaman that he was, would have been well content could the wait have endured uneventful until the light of day again seeped over the mountain ridges. He looked forward to the coming night with unabashed misgiving; yet he made no comment and squirmed about till he had fitted himself snugly against the soft loam, then lay quiet. The sun must already have neared the sea or even, perhaps, have passed beneath; still the flush on Orofena's cloud-cap deepened and the radiance within the valley grew in brilliance and in warmth of tone. In such an air of eerie unreality Tahiti must have been born, and beneath such a vivid sky—the blood-red sky of Oro—its last battle would be fought. Looking out on this strangely blazing world Hoa Pahi slowly shook his head.

"Do you think, son of Tumu-nui, to hide from the gods?"

"No," Rata replied, "but perhaps from those who serve them."

For some while they did not speak, and Rata watched with peculiar fascination the watery veils which were caught from the distant waterfall, then wafted toward them. Pearly gray they had appeared in the light of broad day, but now, in this haunting hour, their color, even their texture had changed. No longer cool mist but finest coral dust they seemed, each smallest particle burning with a soft, incandescent glow. The wavering curtains made their tremulous march from end to end of the valley, dividing it into even segments, into compartments which moved on always with the same slow regularity as if to the unvaried, deliberate tempo of unseen drums. Rata found himself tapping with the fingers of one hand upon the earth. Twenty slow beats—then, briefly, the breath of the falls passed over them. Twenty more, and again they felt the cooling moisture. "Ah," he thought, "the veils of Ihu-ata are measures; measures of the passing moment, of days and seasons: of all time."

Suddenly Rata grasped his companion's arm, and Hoa Pahi started so that his head collided with the Moi above. "What is it?" asked the half dazed steersman.

"Look, and keep silent."

Hoa Pahi looked. He rubbed the top of his head and he kept silent, but his mouth opened and his eyes protruded. Now each of the shimmering, gauze-like drapes bore a living freight! Thousands of tiny beings rode the unsubstantial clouds of spume as humans might ride upon the solid crests of combers of the sea. From side to side they swung, up and down they darted as if clinging to the invisible webs which spiders spin from tree to tree. Hoa Pahi had heard talk of elves for all his life, as who has not, but the reality left him breathless with wonder. How light they were!—creatures made, surely, not of flesh and blood but of air and sunbeams, of star-shine and moon-mist. What grace in their little bodies as they came leaping and tumbling over each other in their merry haste!

What exquisite and fragile music in the myriad small voices which now filled the valley with a sound like tinkling bells! Were these, then, the dread hosts of Ihu-ata? Hoa Pahi could not repress a smile.

By companies and regiments they dropped nimbly to the ground near the fallen Moi. Some, chancing to light among the grasses, were momentarily lost to sight and only the waving green tips showed where they pushed their way through to the open. Others sat upon leaves or clambered onto little stones, and soon a vast army had assembled. The mountain elves consisted, of course, of men and women. Their skins were of an invariable and beautiful shade of brown and their hair was dark as the mountain night. Children were there, too, scampering about quite as do children everywhere, and their size was that of a lowland man's thumb. Babes no bigger than hermit crabs were carried on their mothers' hips, and their occasional wailing and crying was like the altogether insignificant sound which is made by extremely young lizards.

Last to arrive was chief Tuoi and his aid Fefera, who floated in over the heads of their people to drop just before the hollow in which Rata and Hoa Pahi were hidden. The chief removed his minuscule helmet and shook off the dew which weighted the delicate feathers. Then replacing it upon his head, he drew himself up very tall. "Fefera," said he sternly, "Rata has done it again."

"Yes," Fefera agreed, eyeing the king-tree gloomily, "and again we must make the chips fly into the wood, the branches knit themselves to the trunk, the roots drink and the sap flow. We must lift the Moi's head once more from the dust."

"But this cannot go on!" A frown like the tender veins of a new leaf etched the chief's brow. "Are we to become common laborers, we whose homes are Orofena's cliffs, whose food is the sweet air and fresh rain? Are we to go on day after day setting up trees which this stubborn man chops down? Soon shall we be no better than his own subjects who grub and sweat but to fill their big stomachs!"

Big stomachs? The eyes of the two Tahitians crouching beneath the Moi met in some surprise. Hoa Pahi, passing a hand beneath him, felt speculatively of that part of his anatomy. It was an ample stomach without question and, according to elfin standards, would probably be considered fit to consume a mountain of food each day. But Tuoi was hardly fair. A grown man cannot be expected to live on air or the distilled perfume of flowers.

103

"Mark you, Fefera," Tuoi-papa-papa went on, his voice rising till it resembled the cheep of a cricket, "we must put a stop to such trespass. Never before have men dared enter the groves of Ihu-ata, but Rata is without fear, and if others continue after him, the time will surely come when there will be no longer room for us. Imagine, friend! These hulking, slow-footed creatures have the effrontery to call themselves Tahitians—as though this great island were made for their especial benefit!"

"That," said Fefera, "is plainly absurd when everyone knows it was constructed for the sole purpose of holding up this, our mountain valley."

"Everyone does not know it," Tuoi contradicted. "The ignorance of Rata and his people is appalling, simply appalling!"

Ignorant? The eyebrows of the hidden listeners rose and again they turned their heads slowly and looked at each other. Rata's shoulders hunched slightly, then dropped, and if he had spoken he might have said, "Well, who knows, Hoa Pahi? Is there reason, after all, to think the world our private playground?" But Rata kept silence and his attention went back to the two elves who conversed at arm's reach from the leafy barrier through which he peered.

"Yes," Tuoi-papa-papa repeated, "we must put an end to this or we shall find ourselves driven out and become no more than memories. How," he demanded, "how would you like it, Fefera, to find yourself nothing but a fable which men chant about the fires?" Then, since Fefera did not reply, the chief looked down from his six inches on his shorter companion and discovered him standing with a bemused smile on his homely little face. "Ah!" he said in exasperation, "can you not pay attention when I am speaking of serious matters?"

"Excuse me." Quickly Fefera composed his features. "You were saying, Tuoi-papa-papa . . . ?"

Instead of repeating his question Tuoi, whose curiosity was as great as his temper was short, put another. "What was the meaning of that silly smile, my good elf?"

"Why," said Fefera, the corners of his mouth again rising and expanding, "I really cannot help it. Whenever I think . . . whenever I think . . ." The little mite could go no farther. Covering his face with his hands he rocked forward and back while his tiny body trembled with bird-trills of laughter.

"You are the strongest of my elves," the chief declared, "and if I had ten thousand like you I would think little of hoisting up a score of Mois each day, but sometimes I fear your mind is deplorably weak. Do try to control yourself."

Fefera was, as even Rata and Hoa Pahi could see, very strong. The biceps muscles in his arms stood out like small pebbles pushing against the skin. But now, at Tuoi's rebuke, he took a grip upon himself, sighed and wiped the tears of mirth from his eyes. "Aué," he said, "Oh dear—they were so funny. Did you not see the expression on their stupid faces when they saw the tree was up again? Was there ever such a look of dumb amazement as the lumbering helmsman wore? And Rata, too, was obliged to pinch himself to discover if he slept or woke! Really, Tuoi-papa-papa, it is almost worth the labor of putting the Moi in its place to see a thing so comical."

As Fefera spoke the chief's stern expression relaxed, he nodded his head and before the other had finished Tuoi was himself chuckling reminiscently. "Yes, yes," he said, "they were indeed a ludicrous pair," and then they both burst out anew in unrestrained merriment. Their laughter spread to the nearest of the elves and traveled over the entire conclave till all the glen rang with a joyous twittering.

Only the men from down below failed to join in the gaiety. Ludicrous? The king of Tahiti and his foremost warrior? Solemnly they eyed each other. Rata was unused to criticism and a frown creased his brow, which, compared with Tuoi's, was like the furrows of the mountains. But could one be angry with beings the size of fresh-water shrimp? Slowly the frown disappeared and then even Rata and Hoa Pahi smiled. Perhaps Tuoi was right; better to admit that even a king may at times appear slightly ridiculous.

"Well, enough," said the chief of the elves at last. "Fefera, summon the people."

Fefera whipped up a periwinkle shell which was suspended from his shoulder by a blade of grass. He put it to his mouth, puffed out his cheeks and blew. The sound which came forth was, in tone and volume, what might have been expected. Ihu-ata's little folk quieted and listened to their leader.

"Approach, elves!" Tuoi commanded. "Approach and hear how again Rata shall be humbled and our master's Moi planted in the earth." He paused and cast an eye about for a stone from which he might speak with more lofty authority. Not finding one, he hopped up to one of the branches behind which the Tahitians lay. Fefera followed him and then the chief resumed. "First we shall raise the tree. Then we shall roll a great boulder into the mouth of the tunnel which leads to Rata's kingdom. Never again will he set foot within our valley."

A shrill cheer arose at this brilliant strategy, a cheer in which even the babes joined with their inaudible lizard voices. Tuoi-papa-papa smiled with pleasure upon his perch hardly a foot from Rata's face, and Fefera, an equal distance from Hoa Pahi, did likewise. The harangue continued.

"O elves! Come by the thousands, come by the tens of thousands! Come all and with our combined strength we shall . . ." Suddenly Tuoi stopped short. He lifted his head, twisting it from side to side till the feathers of his helmet danced, and he sniffed the air.

"Hold!" he exclaimed in quick alarm. "I smell a man!"

XVII

RATA waited no longer. With careful deliberation he slipped his hand through the foliage and clasped the orator firmly about his middle. At the same time, and with equal care, Hoa Pahi took possession of Fefera. Then they both pushed aside the branches and stepped out.

A gasp of dismay came from the legion of elves, and so great was their panic that in their hurry to escape they tumbled madly one over another, slipping and falling and picking themselves up again to run as fast as their little legs would carry them. One young mother dropped her offspring in her fright and the babe remained alone on a patch of soft moss, bouncing up and down in diminutive fury while tears the size of particles of salt spray coursed down its chubby cheeks. At last the husband, discovering the loss, dashed back to snatch up the weeping bundle, then scurry again after his fellows. They had not gone far, however, when, seeing they were not pursued, they paused in their pell-mell flight. Hiding behind clumps of grass, dried leaves and small flowers they peeped out to see what might have become of their beloved Tuoi and his right-hand elf.

The two captives, meanwhile, were struggling valiantly. They flailed about them with their fists, they twisted and turned. Tuoi-papa-papa squirmed so that his plumed helmet joggled from his head and fell

to the ground, and Rata, stooping, considerately picked it up and put it on again. But Tuoi was in no frame of mind to appreciate small courtesies, and once so far forgot his chiefly dignity as to bite Rata's thumb with a force and determination which could hardly have been bettered by a well-developed but moderate-sized crab. The monstrous hands did not relax their hold. Their owners walked along the Moi till they came to a place where the trunk tapered sufficiently to be of convenient size, and there they seated themselves.

"Now," said Rata, "we are going to have a talk. And it is quite needless to tire yourselves. Why do you not sit still?"

Since both the chief and Fefera were by this time thoroughly exhausted and breathless, their writhings gradually ceased and the lowland men were able to examine them at leisure. Holding them between thumb and forefinger Rata and his helmsman inspected their respective prisoners with undisguised interest and admiration, turning them this way and that, right side up and upside down, feeling of the soft texture of the cobwebby pareus which covered them, testing the muscles in arms and legs, touching the small feet with their attractively splayed toes. But though Hoa Pahi found the perfect little bodies quite marvelous, it was to Fefera's face that he continually returned, and at last he held the perspiring elf close to his own nose the better to study him. With a stubby forefinger the helmsman touched gently the dark brows which grew together in the middle, the delicate ears which stuck out on either side and finally the wide mouth which stretched so far across poor Fefera's face.

Suddenly Hoa Pahi burst into a loud guffaw; so loud it was that Ihu-ata's army started in terror and ducked behind the protecting leaves and flowers. "Ho, ho, ho!" he roared. "Look, Rata; look at this and tell me, have you ever seen anything in all Tahiti quite so homely?"

Rata looked at Fefera and then at Hoa Pahi. "Well, friend," he said with a twinkle in his eye, "if, one day when the lagoon is unruffled, you will but look over the side of your canoe you will have your answer."

Hoa Pahi had often looked into the lagoon's mirror, but always he had been searching for fish and had completely disregarded his own image. Yet he was far from failing to take Rata's meaning, and a hand went quickly to his own mouth while with an expression of pained concern he tested its shape and dimensions.

"Do not be alarmed," Rata smiled. "Neither you nor Fefera were made for beauty, but there are many who love those features and would not change them if they could. But see here." He held up the chieftain on the palm of his hand. "Was there ever such a pompous little fellow as this? Did you notice him when he stood on the branch before us addressing his people? How tall he stretched, how he threw out his nutshell chest, how grandly he strutted and gesticulated! Did you ever lay eyes upon his like?"

It was the seafarer's turn to grin. "Yes," he replied, looking at the big king and the little, "I most certainly have, though somewhat magnified, and it is unfortunate, Rata, that you will never have the pleasure, since you cannot see yourself."

"Indeed!" he replied, a little taken aback. "Indeed!" He stared doubtfully at Tuoi-papa-papa. "Perhaps," he observed finally, "it is just as well and no misfortune at all. Yes, Hoa Pahi, I think it is probably a blessing that we do not see ourselves as others see us. But now let us get down to business. Would you," he inquired of the elfin chief, "be content to sit quietly on my knee if I release you?"

"This is a grievous thing you have done," said Tuoi, who had now recovered his breath and his composure. "Never before have we been touched by the hand of man. You have trodden on tapu ground and you have desecrated our persons."

"That I have," Rata admitted, "but only through great necessity."

"No necessity can be so great," Tuoi replied sternly, "as to justify one's trifling with the gods and their servants."

For the moment Rata left this censure unanswered. "I am glad to see," he remarked, "that you speak the language of Tahiti; so may we in the end come to understand each other."

"Do you hear that, Fefera?" asked Tuoi-papa-papa, twisting around to his second. "Did I not tell you they were very stupid? Speak the language of Tahiti! And what other language is there, pray?"

"Why, none, of course," Rata admitted.

"None but that of beasts and birds and fish," Hoa Pahi put in.

"We are not of those races," Tuoi said with dignity. "We are the people of Ihu-ata. And now if you will take your great hands from about us we will, since there appears to be no alternative, sit for a while on your knees."

The men complied, and once they were liberated the elves set about adjusting their gossamer pareus, which had become badly mussed, and Tuoi-papa-papa righted his helmet, which had slipped till it was cocked over one ear. Fefera, luxuriating in his new-found freedom, began swinging his legs, and all the other little folk who watched furtively from a distance edged a bit nearer, still poised for instant flight if danger threatened.

For some moments, with arms akimbo, Rata contemplated the two sprites in silence. It may have been mere accident that Tuoi-papa-papa had assumed a similar posture and regarded the king of the low country with equal calm. At last Rata spoke. "Tuoi-papa-papa, I must have this Moi for my war canoe, and so I shall if I have to cut it down a hundred times."

"That you shall not, Rata; not if we have to stand it up twice a hundred times." Tuoi's words reached the nearest of his subjects and evoked from them a very faint and timorous little cheer.

"I will have it if I must chop it down twice two hundred times!"

"Not if we are obliged to raise it twice again that number!"

"It shall be mine if I spend the rest of my life in this forest with axe in hand!"

"Never!" Tuoi shrilled. "Never, though we spend all our lives in repairing your destruction!"

"Parau mau!" Fefera cried, "Truly said!" The onlookers, seeing that no harm came to their leaders, were now again close about the tree. "Yes, yes!" they all piped. "Truly said! Parau mau, parau mau!"

"Incidentally," said their chief lowering his voice, "do you happen to know, Rata, what is the life span of an elf?"

"Well, no," the king of Tahiti replied, somewhat crestfallen. "No, not exactly. Is it perhaps similar to that of the butterfly?"

"Hee, hee, hee!" Fefera exploded. "Butterfly! Hee, hee, hee, hee!" A chorus of merry, derisive laughter came from all the slender, reed-thin throats.

"I will instruct you, my poor simple man," said Tuoi-papa-papa, smiling tolerantly. "But first let me ask you a question. When did you first hear of us?"

"Long, long ago," Rata replied. "At my mother's knee when I was very small."

"Precisely. And one day when you and Turia have sons, is it likely that they should grow up in ignorance of us?"

"Impossible, for surely their mother or I myself would speak of you."

Tuoi clapped his hands. "There you have it! It is our peculiarity that we go on just so long as we are thought and spoken of. Even you should therefore be able to deduce that we shall never die."

"Aué, Rata," groaned Hoa Pahi, "I am afraid we are undone," and in sudden discouragement he thoughtlessly allowed both his legs to slide out in front of him. Fefera, caught unawares by the abrupt cataclysm, was toppled from his perch and would have fallen to the ground if he had not made a frantic grab for the seaman's kneecap and clung on for dear life.

"Eh, eh, eh," said the steersman apologetically when he saw what he had done, and, bending over, he rescued the dangling elf, then drew his legs in again and set him down securely. "No harm done, I hope?"

"Never mind," Fefera remarked stiffly, "but it was exceedingly clumsy of you."

A silence fell upon the group, and Rata let his eyes wander gloomily over the darkening grove. Was he to be defeated in spite of all his high hopes and all his confidence by a people none of whom was bigger than his own hand? But what could a man do in one short lifetime against these determined elves to whom fifty years was of no more importance than a single day? The ruddy light was fading, and purple shadows grew at the base of the cliffs, in the caves and hollows and beneath the heavy, thick-leaved plants. It was the somber hour between the setting of the sun and the rise of the great full moon.

"O Tumu-nui," Rata murmured in a momentary excess of melancholy, "O my father, once again you are so distant far. With all my heart I have yearned to win my way to you and gathering up your bones bring them back to this friendly soil. Yet now I sit among the peaks of high Tahiti and my plans, my mission of love, seem crumbling in dust about my feet."

"What is this?" Tuoi-papa-papa inquired, pricking up his ears. "Do I hear you speak of love?"

Rata looked at the chief for a minute as if he had quite forgotten his existence and was obliged to remind himself that there was in truth such a person. Then he nodded slowly and rather sadly. "It is something with which I am afraid you are not familiar. Love, Tuoi-papa-papa, is both grief and joy, pain and pleasure, heartache and delight. It can fill a man with a wondrous tenderness, but so can it lift him to heights of daring and accomplishment. It is a force which works many miracles, and it is strong—even stronger, I had once thought, than your master Ihu-ata." Rata let his voice drop, and ceased speaking. He was sitting somewhat stooped, his shoulders hunched forward, but now with a sigh he straightened. "You would not understand, my little friend; it is really very difficult to explain."

"Not understand!" Tuoi exclaimed indignantly, but with a small catch in his throat, for the elves were very emotional and easily moved to either laughter or tears. "You have no right to say such a thing, Rata! Nor need you trouble yourself with explanations, for who should know better than we the nature of love—we who were created but that there might be such a thing of beauty in the world? And nothing, I can assure you, is more sacred to Ihu-ata and to us than love and reverence of one's parents, one's ancestors. Have you then lost the father who was so dear to you?"

Even the most timid of the elves had now come from hiding, and they gathered in a great half circle about the fallen Moi and the two men who sat thereon. Those on the outskirts stood on tiptoe, pushing forward to miss no word of what was said, and no sound came from them save the occasional shush of a mother quieting a restless child.

"The day was fair," Rata replied, "the sun was bright and I was still young and heedless of all care when noble Tumu-nui sailed away. Long, long we waited, my mother and I; long, long his devoted subjects scanned the lonely sea. We never saw his face again."

A soft moan like a faint stirring of air in the upper branches of the forest rose from Tuoi-papa-papa's company. "You have had no news?" the little chief asked.

"Yes. Hoa Pahi, my father's pilot, has returned with the bitter truth."

"Please let him tell us of it," said Tuoi sympathetically.

And so for a third time Hoa Pahi related his tale of indomitable courage, of death and grim defeat. His narration was frequently interrupted by small cries of horror from his audience, by exclamations of pity and grief and genuine sorrow. One would have thought it was not alone the father of Rata who was lost, but the father of them all. When the helmsman had done, an abbreviated tear trembled on one of Tuoi-papa-papa's lashes, small rivulets ran unrestrained down Fefera's brown face, and many of the women and young girls broke into sobbing lamentation.

Tuoi blew his nose and cleared his throat. "O unhappy man, you have indeed suffered greatly, and this story has sorely wrenched our hearts. You have acted blindly and impulsively, but perhaps not stupidly as I may have intimated. Try, Rata, to forget my unkind words." He paused and wiped his eyes, then continued, "If only you had come with a few bamboo shoots or other offering to Ihu-ata, if only you had made known to him your need, then might you even now be aboard your war canoe making for your perilous goal. For to fulfill such a mission is no disgrace to a king-tree, and it may well be that the seed which held the soul of this tree was planted so that it might sprout and grow through more than two hundred years for the express purpose of sharing in your victory over Pahua. Or," added Tuoi with lowered voice, "to share in a no less glorious downfall. Rata of Tahiti, the Moi shall carry you over the seas!"

Several things then happened all at once. The elves burst into loud acclaim while the youngest among them danced with pleasure and excitement at their leader's decision. Rata sprang to his feet, not forgetting Tuoi-papa-papa, whom he carefully carried with him on his still open palm. And while he stood there seeking words to express his relief, his happiness and gratitude, the moon rose above the highest crags. It shone down into the mystic valley, dispelling the gloom, pouring its soft blue magic indiscriminately over the two human beings and the midget host of Ihu-ata.

"It is our mother," Tuoi explained, "our mother, Hina-in-the-Moon. Do you not know, Rata, how elves are born? No? They unfold like smallest flower petals when Hina tenderly caresses the smooth shaft of Ihu-ata's pinnacle."

"Is it so? Small wonder then that you are such tiny creatures of delight, small wonder that holding you in my hand I seem to clasp no more than a fragment of the moon's elusive light. But let me speak, Tuoi-pa-pa-papa, for my heart is full. Never shall we who live along the fringes of this island forget you and your followers. Word of your goodness and generosity shall travel back across the watery trails to the homeland from which we came and it shall spread as well to whatever new lands the winds may carry us in ages still to come. In the morning I will return with my men to drag the Moi to the shore."

"No, Rata," said the chief with a shake of his head, "that is quite impossible. I cannot permit you to step again within this forest, much less to bring others with you."

The king's face fell. "Not possible? What then is to be done? My helmsman and I, with the best will in the world, can hardly hope to carry it upon our shoulders!"

"No," Tuoi smiled, "that I do not expect. And unless you are as numerous as ants in your villages below I doubt whether all of you together would ever get it to the sea." He beckoned to his aid. "Fefera! A word with you."

Since Fefera now balanced upon Hoa Pahi's palm as did Tuoi upon Rata's, the pilot obligingly stretched forth his hand so that the two elves were able to put their heads together. After a brief whispered consultation, during which Fefera frequently nodded in vigorous assent, Tuoi turned to his people, who looked up to him expectantly.

"Children of Ihu-ata!" he cried, puffing out his chest, and it was again apparent that Tuoi-papa-papa was very fond of public speaking. "Legions of the mountain cliffs and the goddess Hina! Elves by the tens of thousands!" Suddenly, and most effectively, the chief dropped his voice. "Greetings." This preamble was not, perhaps, strictly necessary, but it was the way of a Tahitian whether elf or man. Tuoi took a breath and then went on. "Here is one whose name is Rata. He is a king, but no creature made of moonlight; rather, he is constructed of earth or clay or some other plain material. But he is a good man, and he has a great sorrow. Tell me, all you of Ihu-ata's family, are we to let him go away without lessening his sadness?"

There was a loud chorus of brightly chirping "No's."

"Are we to let him embark on his dangerous quest in a vessel such as the fumbling hands of men would make of this splendid Moi?"

"Never!" they shouted with increasing fervor. "Never!"

Tuoi-papa-papa paused, then he balled his hand into a little fist and suddenly stabbed it skyward. "Let *us* carve the tree! Let *us* braid the sennit! Let *us* hew the planks and mold the hulls and weave the sails, and make a war canoe the like of which the world has never seen!"

Pandemonium broke loose in the hidden valley of the king-trees. Everywhere Rata and Hoa Pahi looked there were leaping, tumbling, moon-swathed elfin figures. Always Tahiti has been a land of bubbling, joyous laughter, of quick enthusiasms and volatile excitements, but never before, and never since, was there such happy and abandoned ardor as atop Mount Orofena on that night. "Yes!" they cried, "yes, yes! We will carve and braid and hew and mold! We shall build a canoe for Rata!" So loud rose their commingled voices that the sound over-ran the valley's rim and flowed down the slopes to waken the slumbering villagers far away by the side of the lagoons. Had all the birds of heaven gone suddenly mad? So many a man asked himself before he rolled over and went again to sleep.

Tuoi-papa-papa twisted round and looked up at Rata with bright eyes, his face flushed and beaming. "Is it any wonder," he asked, "that such fervor can work great miracles?"

"No, Tuoi," he replied, "already I am past surprise."

"Do not be too sure of that," said the chief. Then once more he raised his voice. "Come, elves! Come tall and short and young and old —come all! A thing of beauty we shall build, a thing of grace both fleet and strong. Into it must go the strength and spirit of our Moi and the airy lightness of ourselves. It must mirror the love and determination of this lowland king. It must leap the waves and ride the storms, challenge and attack, vanquish and conquer. It must burn with a life of its very own. Go now, Rata, and look for a rainbow in the morning skies. On its back shall your war canoe be launched, and Vaa-i-ama is its name. Yes, son of Tumu-nui—Ship-of-Flame, that is its name!"

XVIII

RATA felt the cool, downsweeping gust of air which was the breath of mountain rain, and he rushed from the house. The wind ran rough fingers through the dark shock of his hair and he turned his face upward. Large drops of rain—cold, bracing, sparkling—splashed against his cheeks. The day was young, but the sun had risen. It shone past a dark storm cloud which hovered near Orofena's summit, stretching out an arm high over the village. Lightning played from turreted peak to peak of the single cloud in an otherwise clear sky, and thunder rolled from its somber, deep-gouged valleys. Was there a directive message in the heavily echoing voice from above? It may have been so, for though brief driving storms are common even in the early morning hours, the island populace poured into the streets as if obeying a booming summons. Turn your eyes on Orofena, the thunder seemed to peal. Behold the power of the gods and the great marvel they have wrought! Stand silent, as if at prayer, while the hidden beauty of the heavens is made known in form which you of humble, earthly senses may see and understand. Look up, Tahitians, to the skies!

Look up they did, each and every man. Where a moment before had been only empty, blue-vaulted space a vast, far-reaching arc now trembled in the air. Vague it was, at first, blurred and unsubstantial as rain itself. It grew slowly in solidity, in brilliance, till it stood forth a blazing reality bending from the highest of Tahiti's mountains to the shore. It drew to itself the hues of every fish and coral of the broad lagoons, of every bird and flower of the tropic land, fusing and merging them all in a rainbow of such splendor that the eyes of all who watched were dazzled. Then, with a cry of commingled fear and awe and blank astonishment, they saw that where the bridge of gods touched the mountain a shape of radiant light was moving.

"It is my Ship of Flame!" Rata's shout rose loud and clear.

Over the burnished causeway it rode with sails full set, the hulls shining like twin shafts of living fire afloat on a many-colored sea. Star-size in the distance it came steadily on, growing ever larger and more blindingly distinct.

116

THE SHIP OF FLAME

"It is the Moi of Ihu-ata!" Rata exulted. "The king-tree of the cliff god, touched with his magic, is born again!"

As the sacred tree when felled by Rata had dipped earthward first with slow majesty, then with terrifying speed, so now the vessel fashioned of its trunk, reaching the place where the glowing path arched steeply, shot ahead with sudden life. Down it raced like a plunging bird, throwing high and wide from its prows long, curling rainbow streamers, sundering the banded colors over which it flew and flinging them across the sky till all the world was filled with a blaze of red and green and blue and gold.

"It is Vaa-i-ama, my ship of war!" Rata cried once more. Then even he was obliged to close his eyes in the face of such a stabbing brightness. When he opened them again the mighty double-canoe, shining in its coat of raindrops, rested quietly on the ground between the two vessels built by Hotu's artisans.

For a matter of minutes no one in all the village spoke. No one moved. With brains still reeling they stared at the ship descended from the clouds for an island king, at the ship which uncounted elfin hands, working close beneath the moon, had made in a single night. More than twenty feet high rose the carven, knife-edged figureheads at the bows. Well over a hundred feet was stem from stern, and the spear-straight mast would have dwarfed Tumu-nui's own. Never had men built to such a scale. Yet, more astonishing, perhaps, than size was the exquisite craftsmanship apparent in detail. What eel-like slimness to the rounded, smooth-sanded hulls! How easily and swiftly would they part and glide over the waters! Even the building of a small two-man canoe which carries a steadying outrigger at one side is a work requiring both patience and imagination, but to fashion a ship of war, a ship to sail on oceans deeply blue, takes vastly more. Such construction is the task of artists with a love of their material. It should have been no wonder then, at least to Rata and to Hoa Pahi, that the elves had made of their sacred Moi a creation of exalted loveliness, a vessel whose sweeping, sleekly molded lines spoke of proud spirit, of daring, impatience of repose, eagerness to be unleashed upon the sea where winds blow free and all is change and movement.

With something of the same feeling they had experienced when first they set foot within Ihu-ata's forbidden valley they now walked down to stand beside the ship. After some time others began to follow: canoe-builders dumfounded at this highest expression of their trade, fishermen, paddlemen and warriors filled with wordless admiration; men, women and children all pressed forward, yet stopped at a respectful distance to gaze with reverence upon the noble ship of war known then, and ever since through all the annals of history, as Vaa-i-ama.

Slowly, accompanied only by his helmsman, Rata made the circuit of his great canoe, pausing now and then to pass a hand along the polished hulls, marveling at the gloss like hard-rubbed pearl-shell, at the clever joining of the seams so snug that it was nearly impossible to tell where one strip of planking left off and the next began, at the strangely burning color of most vivid red—a color taken from the clays of Orofena or, possibly, from the glowing material of rainbows. Arrived again at the stern, Rata reached his long arms above his head. Tall as he was he was obliged to stand on tiptoe to grasp the gunwale. With a quick flexing of his muscles he pulled himself up, then threw his legs over the side. He bent down and drew Hoa Pahi after him, and together they walked to the steering platform. The helmsman took his place before the forked breech in which Tumu-nui's weathered rudder would soon rest, and Rata stood beside him. So the two would stand through the dark and dangerous days ahead. So they would face each new peril as it came. So, too, they would look on death itself, if such was to be the end.

Two men these were, and no immortals, yet there was no one in all the pressing crowd who did not feel at sight of them a great upsurge of emotion. The one was short and the other tall, yet each in his way a pillar of strength. They might fail, they might sink into oblivion even as had good Tumu-nui, but they were made for glory.

As once before, the people burst into loud, spontaneous acclaim. "Maeva Arii!" they cried, "Hail Rata, King of High Tahiti! Hail Rata and his Ship of Flame!" The din exceeded that which had been heard at the coronation, and doubtless this was as it should be, for it was only now that the island ruler stepped into the fullness of his power. Many a sovereign has worn the maro of ura plumes, but there has been only one Vaa-i-ama in all time, and that was the canoe of Rata. They are inseparable, the man and the ship, and so they have been in all the ages during which bards have lifted their voices by the evening fires to chant of bravery and valor.

Hail then, Rata, for thus you have taken possession of your ship and thus, also, have you grasped your destiny.

XIX

A roller is laid,
A first roller for Oro
To fight the winds.
O far-seeing god,
Now enchant it!

OLD TAHUA'S thin, singsong voice quavered the sacred invocation. It was the day following the miraculous descent of Vaa-i-ama to earth, and a multitude had come from every corner of the island to witness the launching of the fleet. Suiting the high priest's words, a dozen of Hotu's workmen placed a rounded length of timber close before the bows of each canoe.

A roller is laid,
A second roller for Oro
To battle the storm.
Twice served is the winged god;
Now, Oro, enchant it!

One after another, spaced a few feet apart, the logs were laid down the shelving beach.

A roller for Roo the famous,
A roller for Hina the mother,
A roller for Taere of skill,
A roller for Toa-all-knowing;
O Oro—enchant them!

The workmen placed the final lengths of hard tamanu where they were lapped by the green waters of the lagoon, and Tahua raised his blue-veined hands above his head.

> *The last roller is laid,*
> *The roller for Tu, the great father*
> *Who made stable the sky.*
> *It shall smite the great surging waves,*
> *It shall turn them when they strike amidships,*
> *Turn them when they strike behind,*
> *Turn them when they strike the sennit in the bows.*
> *Oro, enchant!*
> *Oro, supporter of the rollers,*
> *Now enchant them all!*

A score of men were gathered about each of the smaller vessels with the sennit launching cords gripped in their hands. Twice that number stood ready beside Vaa-i-ama awaiting their king's command. No sooner had the priest's voice died away than Rata's cry came loud and imperative.

"A tó!" he shouted, "Draw! Draw, my warriors, and may the canoes drink of the sea!"

The men strained at the red-brown ropes and the three ships began their rumbling descent.

"If I sail through breaking waves," Rata intoned, "let them pass under; let the canoes pass over. If I sail through towering seas, let them pass under; let the canoes pass over!"

Gathering momentum as they went, the flagship and the two escorts charged across the sloping strand and into the southern ocean for which they had been made. The hollowed hulls resounded with the solid impact, and from under the bows columns of white-flashing spray shot up to the mastheads, then fell like gentle rain the length of the bared and waiting decks. So drank the vessels of Rata's fleet, tasting from end to end the salt flavor of the sea.

For some time the king remained watching from the shore while the ships ceased gradually their violent plunging and pitching to rest at last, serene and upright, upon the smooth lagoon. Crewmen went aboard, and soon the canoes rode to anchor seaward and to hawsers stretched to coco palms aft.

Rata stepped near the chief of his priests. "A fair sight, is it not, Tahua?"

"It is," the old man replied. "Both brave and fair. Such also," he added after a short pause, "was your father's fleet when it lay in this same sheltered place."

"Never have you said truer word. To my young eyes his ships looked every bit as unconquerable as do my own."

"Yet they succumbed and were torn apart." Rata was silent and the priest went on, "I have never been able to understand it, for at that time the omens were good. I read the signs with care and they told of a safe voyage and a safe return. Rarely have I known it to happen, but on that day a lying spirit must have entered our marae."

"And what auguries have you now?" Rata asked.

Tahua turned away his rheumy eyes. "Of that," he remarked evasively, "who can tell?"

"That can you, I believe." Rata shot the wizened old man a keen look. "I would have an answer."

"I can tell you nothing."

"What!"

"Nothing," the other repeated miserably.

"Last night, as is always done before our people set to sea, did you not put sennit to sleep beneath the sacred stone?"

"I did."

"And this morning when you removed the slab what did you find? Was the woven strand straight or crooked?"

"Neither straight nor crooked; neither twisted nor turned nor as I left it."

"Do you jest with me?" Rata demanded sternly.

"It is no jest."

"Then what is the meaning of your childish conundrum?"

Tahua was plainly in real distress. Nervously he twisted the long fringe of his cape, shifting the glance of his close-set little eyes this way and that, but never meeting the penetrating look of his king. "Ah, Rata," he said at last, facing him and trying to control the trembling of his voice, "it means that I who have seen you grow from a babe in arms to the greatest of Tahiti's kings have been afraid to read the word of the gods. I have not lifted the stone."

"Not lifted . . ." Rata began in disbelief, then suddenly the meaning of the man's halting confession dawned on him. Love of his king had kept him from consulting the age-old oracle. But even in the face of this revelation, Rata could summon no affection for the priest of Oro. Respect, yes; that and reverence too he had been taught to hold for the servants of the marae since he was a child. Yet, like all others from warrior to humble fisherman or plaiter of roofing thatch, he could feel no more. For Tahua's religion, potent as it might be, was stern and cruel. Many of the temple rites were harshly brutal, and often in his long life Tahua's now palsied fingers had dripped with the blood of humans flung upon the merciless, cold altar stones. The priests of Oro, steeped in the ancient cult, lived apart from all other men, guarding jealously their secrets, their wizardry and the hideous idols ranged about the skull-lined walls. Affection for such as these? No, it was impossible.

"I appreciate your concern for me," said Rata, "but in ignoring the prophecies of the buried sennit do we not belittle the gods themselves? That I should not like to do at the outset of so precarious an adventure. Rather shall I go with you to the marae to see with my own eyes what you uncover."

"Very well," Tahua replied, bowing his bald head submissively, "we shall do as you say. You are right in your decision, and I am ashamed of my fears. It will never benefit a man to turn a deaf ear or avert his eyes when the gods would speak or make a sign." So saying he turned upon his heel and led the way back through the village and out along the wide, well tended path toward the grove of mape trees which cast heavy shadows about the marae grounds.

Within a bare five minutes they stood before the forbidding encircling wall; and though the distance they had come was short, the traverse of an ocean could have produced no more marked a change in scene and atmosphere. Here were no shouts of playing children, no grunts and squeals of pigs, no scratching fowls, no friendly crackling cooking-fires. There was no sound to tell of the ordinary lives and intercourse of human kind. Instead was hush and silence with the air grown dim; dim because of the hemming trees and dim also, perhaps, because this was an outpost region between two worlds—a place where fanatic priests gazed endlessly into a murky, mysterious, unfathomable beyond. What are the thoughts of the dead departed, what those of the ruling gods and what their plans for little men? Watch the blood patterns on the altars, study the entrails of the slaughtered pig, follow the flight of cloud and fall of meteor, harken to the cry of birds and insects, to the speech of wind-moved leaves. All hold secrets, all hold meaning. But what secrets, what meaning? Peer, peer, priests of old Tahiti, into the great obscurity, into Te Po—the Land of Night—and seek there to read the truth.

Rata and Tahua passed through a narrow opening in the wall and into the large courtyard with flagging of smooth stones. Oppressive in its frowning bulk, the temple rose before them, a man-made mountain of coral and limestone rock. Hundreds of years had passed over the marae, as the number of upright stone slabs in the court, each symbolic of some departed monarch, testified. Hundreds of years had passed

since men by the thousand sweated and toiled to raise so massive a monument to the powers of darkness. Yet Rata never stepped within the walls of stern tapu without a feeling of admiration for the zeal of those who built.

The marae was of pyramidal form based upon a rectangle measuring more than two hundred feet in length and some hundred in width. As it mounted, the entire structure converged in a series of enormous step-like terraces. Clearly, so holy an edifice was not intended to be easily scaled, for each rise was of height such that a man's outstretched arms could not measure it. Ten in number, the giant stairs led on to a summit where only priests and kings might tread.

Now, with ever fresh wonder, Rata looked at the huge blocks of solid rock fitted together with such uncanny nicety. "How do you suppose, Tahua," he asked, "that our ancestors raised such weights as these?"

The high priest continued to thread his way between the altars, both wood and stone, on which fish, coconut and taro were spread upon green leaves. "Those who work for the gods," he replied without turning his head, "are given of their strength." Then, having reached the temple's base, and as if to give point to his words, he began to clamber upward with an agility surprising in one so old. Like a small, angular spider he mounted from deserted terrace to terrace. When religious rites were in progress, each notched ledge of the marae was closely packed with worshipers, but now Tahua was free to pick his path, zigzagging this way and that wherever the better footing offered.

Rata was not far behind, but when the priest vaulted the coping and disappeared within the sunken holy of holies which ran along the temple's crest, he paused to look below. Two buildings shared the clean-swept quadrangle with the many altars. One, standing close against the outer wall, housed the servitors of the marae as well as many of the more sacred relics. The other, on the seaward side, held the barge of Oro. About this structure there gathered a group of temple craftsmen who placed the last strips of pandanus thatch on a small, pole-borne ark. Rata recognized them from the darkness of their skins and the hairiness of their bodies: the Opu-nui or August-stomachs, chosen for these very characteristics and so named because it was their privilege to consume the food offered to the gods. He recognized, too, the portable shrine on which they worked; before that day's sun had set it would house a small replica of the idol which was the marae's reason for existence and it would rest firmly lashed between the bows of his own canoe. The time was near, near. He cast a fleeting glance to the village. The houses were hidden behind the trees but a few columns of lazily mounting wood-smoke showed where it lay, where the simple life went on. Someone was

probably heating stones for the earth-oven, or roasting a freshly speared fish or even a suckling pig. Would he see again the many clustered, peak-roofed dwellings which lined the sunny shores? And the many faces; those that were beloved, those that stood for friends, those that were merely familiar—were they to be seen once more on a day still to come?

Rata turned. Grasping the parapet which separated him from Oro and his oracle, he gave a spring and dropped within.

A long narrow corridor lay open to the sky before him. At the far end where Oro's monstrous wooden likeness loomed head and shoulders above the surrounding bastions, Tahua had already prostrated himself before the blank-eyed, leering idol. Rata made his way toward him past the row of upright leaning-stones for praying priests and the larger ones reserved for king and queen, past the little foot-high stones by which coconut-leaf puppets kept constant vigil, past the pedestaled temple drums, so tall that to beat upon them a man must mount a platform. Just beyond lay the images of twin sharks black-charred by sacred fire —brothers of those which, at Rata's coronation, had come to touch his skin. Oro had no lack of silent, staring company within his rock-rimmed temple: small bird-images surrounded the fish, countless grinning little idols festooned the walls and, spaced at regular intervals on either side of the long passage, there rose tall plaques of intricately carved and close-grained wood, each one terminating in a forked and double god-head.

When Rata came close beside him the groveling priest got to his feet and looked at his king significantly. Lifting his face to the mute, impassively towering idol, Rata spoke the words expected of him.

"Oro, speak to us and let us know what you intend!"

Tahua bent and grasped a flagstone which lay between the image's enormous feet. "May the sennit lie straight and fair," he muttered, "that the path of our king be likewise."

Slowly, carefully, he lifted the slab and placed it to one side. Both men dropped to their knees. Tahua blew away the white sand in which the sennit was partially buried till the slender woven strand stood forth clear and distinct. For a long moment they stared in silence while high above them the inscrutable, unseeing eyes of Oro stared also, gazing with cold, dispassioned unconcern into the land of eternal night where the doings of men are of importance equal to those of minnows.

At last the high priest raised his glance to meet his sovereign's. There was a twitching at one corner of his mouth and his bald head shook visibly on his thin, scrawny neck. "Perhaps," he faltered, "perhaps, Rata, a lying spirit has again entered into our marae . . ."

The muscles of Rata's jaw had hardened; his expression was grim, but he spoke quietly. "Save your breath, Tahua," he said. Then, turning his back on priest and idol—and upon the sennit which lay tortuous as twisting centipede or writhing eel—he set off for the village, his ships and warriors.

XX

BOARD YOUR SHIPS, men of Tahiti!" The call resounded through the streets. "Tahitians—to your war canoes!" Conch shells trumpeted, drums began their steady thud. "Chosen men of Rata, walk down to the sea!"

The summons penetrated the bamboo walls of every home and it penetrated, too, the spacious house which Tumu-nui once had built. Three people sat upon the sanded floor of the oval dwelling, sat much as they had on a certain day many months before, except that Turia was not now among them. There was Iore, who drew idle patterns in the sand only to erase them with an impatient palm. There was Rata's mother, who held again in her slender hands the fine pandanus of a nearly finished basket. And there was the young king himself. With vigor, and as if to forestall the need of speech, he passed a strip of shark skin back and forth over the shaft of wood he gripped. But this was not a bow, not a thing made for a pleasing, graceful sport; and it had no need of further polish. It was the eighteen-foot spear barbed with jagged teeth given him at his coronation, and it was a weapon made to kill.

"On board, warriors, paddlemen! Tighten your maros and take up your arms. On board!"

The call was near and loud, and the three beneath Tumu-nui's roof could no longer ignore it even if they had had a mind to do so. Queen

Maemae put aside her weaving, Iore folded his lanky arms about his knees. Rata placed the spear on the ground, where it lay beside the heavy battle axe with which he had chopped down the Moi.

"My son," said Queen Maemae softly, "it is strange and pitiful that when so few minutes remain to us we must sit in silence. But so it is always when the heart is full to breaking. The wrench of parting and the thoughts which it sends whirling through our minds leave us stunned and mute. Once you are gone, once the mast of your canoe has sunk from sight—ah, then, when there are no ears to hear, words will come, words as numerous as the sands, to speak my love and anguish, my pride and happiness. Be not surprised that I think of happiness at such a time, for with all the pain mine is great, great. Hard as it is for me to see you leave, I would not have it otherwise."

There was a sudden commotion at the doorway, a rattling at the eaves as if the dried fronds were torn by a gust of wind.

"Who goes there?" Rata called.

"Hoa Pahi. I have come for the helm."

"Take it, Friend-of-the-Ship, take it!"

They heard a grunt as Hoa Pahi lifted the long, heavy paddle to his shoulder and then his gruff question, "You are coming?"

"Yes, yes," Rata replied. "Soon."

"Soon?" said his mother. "No, Rata, I must keep you no longer. The ship given you by the elves is waiting as are all your people. Go to them, my son. Go now, for you shall not sail with a picture of Queen Maemae which is marred by weak tears; that I would not have. But you must hurry, dear one; you must go quickly, quickly, because I do not trust myself."

Once before Rata had looked into the large brown eyes even as he did now. Drenching rain had filled the world with sodden gloom and a bird of paradise had screeched its chilling cry. With a shock he had read his mother's fear, and such he saw again today. Yet only the dull in spirit, he now knew, may part from those who are loved without its clutching at the heartstrings. Is it to be for always, the inner voices question, is this the end?

"Iore," said Rata quietly, "take my weapons and place them aboard Vaa-i-ama. Tell Hoa Pahi to make ready to weigh anchor." Without comment Iore picked up spear and battle axe and carried them out. Mother and son were left alone.

A few brief moments later Rata strode briskly the beach leading to the cove which his mind now held as his and Turia's alone, and he smiled with satisfaction at his own sure insight. Turia's absence from the village had caused him no disquiet; he knew well where he should find her. Hurriedly he made his way across the point and came out upon the shelving beach on the leeward side. He started toward the fara tree—and then halted in dismay. She was not there.

More slowly then, unable to believe, he went on till he stood beneath the outspread branches, beneath the fan-like clusters of leaves of which roofing thatch is made. He looked down at the small, long-unused canoe, at the petals of withering, still-fragrant tiare scattered on white sands which their bodies had pressed so short a time before, and he said, speaking low, "Turia, do you so soon forget our meeting place?"

"I am here, Rata."

He raised his eyes to find her lying against the same leaning bough as on the day of his tender youth when he had thought to share in Tumunui's fortune. Impatient he had been then and impatient, in how different a way, he was now. He stepped to the base of the tree. "Come down, Turia-itie," he cried. "Slip down, beloved, where I may hold you closely!"

He caught her up before her feet had touched the ground. "So," he laughed, "would I carry you aboard."

"Yes," she said, knowing well the impossibility, "take me. Take me with you!"

"Then should I have no reason for return."

Her face clouded at his words and she clung to him fiercely. "You will come back," she said in a tone tinged with defiance. "You will come back to me!"

He lowered her so that she stood before him but still clasping him tightly. With his hands he gathered her hair and brought it forward so that it made a nebulous frame about her upturned face. "Surely," he told her earnestly, "no man has lived who had more awaiting him at home. The days will pass; watch for the rising of our sails."

"Aué, I shall."

He smiled. "Together we must place children on the land."

"Many children!" she agreed.

Some while later Rata took her arms gently from about him. "Remain," he said simply, paused, then turned and walked swiftly away.

He had reached the point when she called after him. "Go, Rata! Go . . . !" He raised a long brown arm before he passed from sight.

"WHAT NOW, TAHUA?" Rata demanded. "Are we to have more of your bad omens?" He stood at the water's edge beside the barge on which rode the ark of Oro. Crowded close about and lining the shores of the bay both north and south were the people of Tahiti.

The high priest made no reply but strode waist-deep into the lagoon. In one hand he held a ripe coconut, in the other a knife of stone. Expertly he slashed the outer husk, then held up the firm round shell for all to see. With another stroke of the knife he split the nut in two. As if the two halves of the shell were small toy boats, he placed them in the sea with the cupped white meat uppermost; then he pushed them under.

"Sink," he croaked, "sink down. But turn not over! Let not two shells capsize lest the king's ship be engulfed. Let not one capsize lest great peril make the outcome a thing of clouded doubt. Ride down, shells, evenly . . . unturning . . ."

All who were near watched with bated breath as the coconut halves, white and clear in the untroubled water, dropped toward the bottom. One descended more quickly than the other, straight and true till it was safely at rest. But the second, perhaps smaller and lighter, began a slow oscillation which widened and grew more rapid. Amid the groans of the spectators it then flipped over to lie, a small dark mound, against the level sands.

"So our fate is in doubt, Tahua?" Rata spoke so that not only those on shore but also those standing at the ships' rails could hear. "Good! I do not ask for more. What should give greater zest, what greater strength to our arms than the knowledge that the balance between success and failure is finely drawn? But enough of your prophecies and your talk of doom. Where is the priest who rides with me on Oro's barge to step aboard and share my Ship of Flame?"

Tahua took a step forward. "I am your man," he said simply.

"You! Do you then take so lightly your own warnings?"

"I make light of nothing."

"Then you appreciate the danger."

A faint, ironic smile curled the priest's lips. "Would you expect one who counts his years by scores to cling to life with unseemly deter-

131

mination while those who, like yourself, have hardly tasted its full flavor risk it gladly? If such is your thought, Rata, you pay me no compliment. I have grown old in the service of the marae, old and withered and enfeebled. But the time has left me with an experience of many mysteries. This expedition is hemmed by dark shadows and great care must be taken with the idol which you carry. Leave that to me and turn me not away."

"Turn you away?" said Rata with new-found admiration. "That I shall not do. Mount the barge, Tahua; take your place."

The priest obeyed and the king followed him. Then, with the great temple drum sounding, the barge moved slowly over the water to the waiting ships. The ark of Oro with its sacred contents was lifted to Vaa-i-ama and lashed firmly between the bows. One by one the small outriggers which clung to the sides detached themselves from the double canoes and made for shore. Rata walked to the stern and mounted the platform beside Hoa Pahi and Iore, who was the last to go. His uncle came up to him, cleared his throat as if for a parting word, then stood irresolute.

"You have brought the weapons?" said Rata, trying to ease the older man's distress.

Iore nodded and pointed to the gunwale. There, propped against the rail, were the battle axe, the spear and also, Rata noted with some surprise, the bow and quiver with which he had won the archers' meet. He smiled at this fresh testimony of his uncle's pride in that event.

"It seems small enough when placed beside you today," said Iore who followed Rata's glance. "But it is the symbol of your budding strength; take it with you that it may witness the full flowering."

Briefly the two men embraced. Then Iore broke away and stepped over the side to the still-waiting barge.

"Up anchors!" Hoa Pahi shouted and in each ship strong hands heaved at the hawsers, drew in the heavy stones. He faced shoreward. "Cast off!" he called. Three men freed the lines which were bound to the stout boles of as many coco palms. Hand over hand they were drawn aboard. Solemn-faced and silent the people watched as this last connection with the land was severed, leaving Rata's fleet floating free upon the gently rising and falling surface of the bay.

Suddenly the silence was broken by a single cry. "You will conquer, O Rata; you will return triumphant!" It was a girl's high treble and it voiced with clear courage the desperate hope to which all held but which none had dared express.

Rata turned and looked. She stood in the forefront of the sober crowd where the lagoon wavelets lapped her bare feet. The breeze stirred the tresses of her hair, the light of the westering sun shone on her youthful face, making of her lips a curve both warm and full; in her eyes was a dancing brightness. It was she who had once waited for a lad called Rai, for Rai who had gone with Tumu-nui. Was it only yesterday that Rata had seen her serving his mother with the sorrow of her loss still plain upon her face? Now, forgetful of self, she called her brave farewell. "Conquer, Tahitians—conquer and return!"

Something of her indomitable spirit carried to all those who manned the three canoes. A loud answering cheer came from their throats and they swung the paddles, sending the vessels toward the sea.

Rata turned to his helmsman. "Well, Friend-of-the-Ship, are you now content?"

"Content?" A broad smile spread over Hoa Pahi's sun-darkened features. "Rata, I have lived for this day!"

Serenely the ships moved on till they had covered two thirds of the distance to the barrier reef. "We will make sail," Hoa Pahi remarked, "as soon as we have cleared the pass. If the wind holds . . ." He was interrupted by a sudden disturbance below. There was a rumbling sound in the hold as of shifting cargo and then the cries of running seamen. The paddles stopped and the canoes drifted. Those on shore who had begun to turn away hurried back to stare with misgiving at the halted ships. Was Rata's fleet so soon following in the exact pattern of his father's?

Two warriors appeared holding a prisoner between them, and they brought him to the foot of the steering platform. "Rata," said one, "he was hidden among the breadfruit."

Rata looked down on the man sternly; then, abruptly, his expression changed. "Tavae!" he exclaimed, "Tavae of Huahine!"

The other lifted his face. "Yes, Rata, it is even so."

"Among the breadfruit!" Rata burst out laughing. "If you had asked me, Tavae, I could have told you it is a poor hiding place. Why are you here?"

"Almost a month ago," he replied, "word reached our island that your fleet was building. Well I knew the reason why and I longed to join you. For days I have lived in the hills close to your village; this afternoon, unnoticed, I came aboard."

"You should have spoken."

"That I feared to do. It is not always a stranger is wanted on such a voyage."

"But you are no stranger, man. Have we not drawn bows together on the archers' field?"

Tavae's face brightened; yet he answered with his customary reserve. "You mean . . . ?"

"That you are welcome. Mount here beside me!" He bent and took the other's wrist and with an agile leap Tavae gained the platform. "What more could a king ask than a man like yourself on his left and Hoa Pahi on his right?"

The current had carried the vessels to the mouth of the pass. Now the helmsman eyed the frothing tongues of the reef. He took a deep breath into his powerful lungs. "Set sails!" The tightly woven mats rose up, and with Rata's Ship of Flame in the lead the three war canoes bore away into the setting sun.

Only once the king looked behind and then it was to scan the summit of the mountain known as Orofena. "Are you watching, Tuoi-papa-papa?" he murmured. "Are you there in the tallest Mois with Fefera and all your many people? Do you see the ship which you have made and named lifting to the deep sea's swell? Then touch it once again with your wondrous elfin magic, breathe upon the sails your myriad flower-scented breaths and send us on!"

Vaa-i-ama came out from the lee of the land and caught the full strength of the brisk trade wind which travels the vast unobstructed wastes of the Pacific. She heeled sharply and leaped forward across the darkening ocean.

XXI

FOR TWO DAYS the fleet of King Rata of Tahiti continued southward with fair and quartering winds. From all three vessels the bow waves curled whitely, and the sun shone bright upon the intense blue sea. Vaa-i-ama kept the lead, but the two smaller ships were close astern. Almost four hundred souls filled the three canoes, and no man suspected how soon their number was to be cut in half.

The morning of the third day dawned to disclose clouds clinging low on the circling horizons. By afternoon those to the west had begun a slow ascent of the sky. When at last they hid the sun Tahua ceased the low, keening chant which he had kept up for long monotonous hours. He sat on his heels close to the ark of Oro, his chin resting upon his knees, which were doubled up close against his narrow chest. Without so much as turning he pronounced, "Long-wave and Short-wave are coming."

His voice carried aft where Rata, Hoa Pahi and Tavae were seated on the deck before the tiller. A seaman was at the helm. Hoa Pahi looked into the heavens.

"Yes," he observed, "it does not require a priest to tell that we shall have squalls tonight. Perhaps more than squalls." He turned back to the chart which he had spread out on the deck between them. Hoa Pahi's chart was roughly square and crisscrossed from side to side with many lines. It was made entirely of carefully measured, carefully tied dried reeds. "As I was saying," he resumed, "this heavily knotted place from which so many stems diverge is Tahiti."

"I see," said Tavae, who was himself not versed in navigation. He placed a finger on the intersection of two reeds. "Then this must be Huahine."

"Exactly. A sail of a day and little more, as you know."

"And where," said Rata, "is Revareva to which you and my father voyaged?"

"Here," the helmsman indicated.

"So far?"

"It is far," Hoa Pahi agreed. "Nearly ten times the distance from Tahiti to Tavae's birthplace."

Both Rata and Tavae studied the chart with interest, and the man from Huahine scratched his head. "It is very ingenious, Hoa Pahi, but do you mean to say that with no more than this flimsy arrangement of reeds you can raise the smallest and most distant island?"

"No," he admitted. "For short voyages no more is necessary. You have yourself come several times to Tahiti and have seen that for such a trip it is enough to know the time of year and to observe the course of the sun. Tahiti is large and its mountains tall; you cannot miss it. But suppose the place you seek is far away, and suppose it rises no more than a few feet above the sea. To come upon such a spot you must read the stars as well. And even so," he added after a moment, "it is very difficult and far from sure. Many a man has failed to find his island and has drifted on to die of thirst beneath a blazing sun."

"Of course," Rata interrupted. "Everyone knows that the bones of our people make paths on the bottom of every sea. If it were not so, is it likely our ancestors would have found the lands we now call home? But where, Hoa Pahi, is our goal? Lay your hand upon the chart and show it to me."

The older man smiled faintly at his king's impatience and made no immediate move to comply. "That I cannot do exactly," he replied. "I know how many days passed after your father and I left the fertile island where we were so well received. During the first part of the voyage we had a breeze much like that which sends us forward now. On the last fatal day we moved with paddle alone. So I can estimate the distance we had covered. Yet in some manner we had strayed from our true course, for, as I have told you, never before had we seen the two atolls upon which Pahua fastens. I can guess but that is all." He leaned over the chart, letting his eyes run along the brown reeds which marked the paths of many a double canoe and many a simple outrigger. "It should be," he said slowly, "just about *here*," and he stabbed his finger at a spot almost midway of the route to Revareva.

Rata nodded. "Two nights and two days sailing."

"With fair winds, yes." Again the steersman looked aloft. He did not like what he saw. The dark-centered clouds had risen higher and now spread over half the sky. "But such we are not to have." He rose, and walking aft dismissed the seaman and himself took the tiller. Rata followed and stood beside him while Tavae carried the chart below.

"This is not the season of storms," Hoa Pahi remarked, "and on that account it may not last long, yet while it does it may be all the more severe."

Rata folded his arms across his chest. "I have faith in Vaa-i-ama and in yourself, Hoa Pahi. Let it blow."

"That is all very well to say, and still the best of ships have foundered if Long-wave and Short-wave chanced to catch them in between." As he finished speaking the wind, which had held so steadily since the outset of the voyage, faltered. After a moment's lull it came on again, but gustily, and from a few points farther south.

Rata turned to his friend. "You are troubled," he said.

"Not for ourselves; at least not greatly. I never waited for a tempest with my feet upon a more solid ship. But the others are less able." The sea was already making up, and Hoa Pahi looked dubiously across the stretch of tossing water which separated them from the two vessels built by Hotu's workmen. They, too, were staunch and their sennit firm-tied. But how small they appeared in the fading light, how small and yet how gallant as they rose to each succeeding wave and then slid down into the trough to knife the next with their sharp bows, charging the black seas and flinging them disdainfully to either side in clouds of wind-caught spray.

Rata, also, felt a pang of doubt as he watched them. Would they be there when the sun rose to another day? Would they? But there is no need to question. "No," he thought with a sudden feeling of exultation, "it has always been so. That is the way of the world, the way of my race and people. Some will survive, some will not, but they will always keep on battling whatever the gods may offer. In ships like these my ancestors came from the land of our birth; in ships like these, in my own lifetime, men of Tahiti have found Burning Havai'i, where the mountains spout bright fire. This voyage as well may live on after us . . ."

Impetuously he cupped his hands to his mouth and shouted loud and strong down wind to his faithful men following in their lesser craft. "Deep with the paddles, firm with the helm! Face the storm, pierce the wind—pass over, not under!"

The answering cry was faint in the gathering gale. Yet none aboard Vaa-i-ama failed to hear it: "Life to you, Rata—long life!"

Rata strained his eyes trying to distinguish the faces of those on the other ships. But if the vessels were small, the figures dotting the decks now appeared in the widening distance no larger than so many elves of Ihu-ata. Briefly the clouds which lay before the setting sun thinned, so that both canoes were limned against a narrow strip of shining, wave-dented horizon. For the moment they stood out in clear silhouette of black and white, and Rata saw that in the bows of one a man had climbed the vertical figurehead. At one instant he was hidden in a dark valley of the sea and at the next he was tossed up against the bit of brilliant sky. His arm was raised, and he waved it back and forth in last salute. The clouds closed in again, and Rata turned away. It seemed to him that he had no sooner done so than starless night shut down, separating the canoes one from the other, leaving each alone with its own struggle, its own storm and its own fate. The blackness was so intense that every man was hidden from his neighbor, and not even Hoa Pahi, who stood but a foot away, remarked the tears of pride and anguish which filled the eyes of the king.

Aboard Vaa-i-ama the sail had been lowered, the paddles again manned. Though the vessel pitched and rolled there was as yet no danger and Hoa Pahi called to the crew, "Slowly!—give me steerageway, no more. Save your strength for what is yet to come." So they waited, but not for long. The sound of the wind came before it struck, and an awful sound it was; a deep-throated roaring in the distance, which rose to a whining screech as it neared.

Unseen by the others, Tavae had felt his way back to take his place at Rata's side. He leaned toward the steersman. "Hoa Pahi! Shall I add my weight to the helm?"

138

Rata's pilot held the grip of the long oar flat against his hairy chest. With one foot against the gunwale, he stood braced to meet the hurrying tempest. "No, Tavae," he said through clenched teeth. "When Pahua sundered Tumu-nui's canoe it did not break my hold upon the helm, else I should not be here now. No mere storm shall throw me."

"Well said, Friend-of-the-Ship!" Rata exclaimed. "But we go to meet no ordinary storm."

"True," Hoa Pahi agreed. "This bids fair to be one worthy of Vaa-i-ama. Steady now!"

The wind fell upon them like a solid, heavy weight, but it was a weight that lived, that tore and rended like a thing possessed. Its savage breath, chill from the polar icecaps, goaded the sea to frothing turmoil, sent it charging against the double canoe in rank upon rank of mountain wave and canyon trough. Vaa-i-ama's proud carved stems tilted up till pointed almost directly at the unrelieved black of the arching heavens. Here, while the rows of paddlemen bent low with bodies parallel to the bulwarks, she paused trembling as a great comber fell away, leaving the forward third of her sleek, dripping hulls suspended free in the wind-cursed air. Then suddenly, as if thrown forward by a giant hand, she smote with jarring, crashing report the backside of the wave and plunged down, down for the inky center of the sea, down for the center of the globe, for the land of the dead—Te Po itself. When it seemed the dizzying descent could end only in disaster, the twin cutwaters bit into the next approaching wall to gouge a foaming, spray-drenched path, and with a shudder the vessel began to mount once more.

"Up!" Rata shouted, "up, Ship of Flame; climb again into the sky!"

Hoa Pahi's wide, thick lips were curled back in a fierce smile. "She will rise," he bellowed. "She is a fighting ship! Give me your strength, paddlemen!" But in Rata's ear he cried, "They are not in unison—no man can see his fellow!"

Without reply Rata seized Tavae by an arm, dragged him to the lower deck and thrust a paddle in his hands, snatched up another for himself. They rushed for the gunwales and sank the blades in the churning sea.

"Ahoe!" Rata cried, "Ahoe—stroke—stroke—stroke!" In time now with the rhythmic call of their king, the men swung their paddles.

"Ahoe, ahoe!" Vaa-i-ama pushed on into the eye of the storm. But Rata's guiding voice had sounded only briefly when stinging, swirling, suffocating rain choked it in his throat. The paddles paused, the ship slowed, faltered. His toes digging at the canting deck like tough stub fingers, Hoa Pahi fought to keep the bow pointing for that distant hole in the horizon from which his senses told him the winds poured. Hold fast, determined and homely-visaged man! Made by the hands of ten thousand elves though she be, let the ship of Rata veer but once, let her broach to and take but one murderous sea broadside, and all is done. Hoa Pahi knew, and as the disorganized and almost helpless vessel careened into the next cliff-sided valley, he whipped the thiry-foot oar back and forth in wide, quick sweeps as though it were no more than a slender pole made for pushing a fragile outrigger. But for all his strength and all his skill, the stern swerved out dangerously, as if it were sucked aside by a magnet which nothing could resist. They rose to a crest, and to another and another, and each time despite Hoa Pahi's knotted, bulging muscles the course of the ship became wilder, more uncontrolled. One man could not do it all, and he roared aloud: "To-gether now! Ahoe!" Like Rata's, the leather-lunged voice of the helms-man was drowned in the maelstrom of flying scud and rain.

But there came an answer to the desperate call. Faint and uncer-tain at first, it soon steadied and swelled. It cut through the din of screaming shrouds, the howl of wind and thundering collision of the waves, to strike the ears of every man aboard. It seemed to lift the en-compassing blackness and to show a guiding light. Each one was drawn to his brother, each one found fresh vigor, and all the scores of rowers were knit again in a single, conscious whole. It was the drum of Oro! Within the close confines of the pandanus shrine, reeling in the dark be-fore his god of paint and twisted sennit, Tahua had picked up the paddle-beat set by the king. Now with the flat of his aged palms he pounded it out on the taut hide cut from the belly of a shark. Did that heartening, life-giving sound come from the hands of a palsied and enfeebled man? To Rata, bending his back in rhythm with the rest, it seemed as if the old priest had seized upon the loosed fury of the hid-eous night to fling it all upon the quivering head of his echoing hol-lowed log. Whether he knew it or not it was deep and telling magic which Tahua wrought in his frenzy, and at each resounding boom the ca-noe surged forward as though he and his instrument alone were the pro-

pulsive force. Though the gale increased, though it rose to a final rav-
ing tumult when sky and sea were merged in one crazed whirl of wrack
and spume, the pigmy, man-made thunder of Oro's drum would not be
silenced, but throbbed on announcing to a world gone mad that here
Tahitians rode the sea!

XXII

A TROPIC DAWN is a sudden, spectacular shift from night
to day. There is no gentle lingering of blue darkness, no
soft, slow-budding flush spreading fan-like in the east. As
on the fertile islands sprinkled over the southern seas the
plants, and men as well, spring up quickly to ripe matu-
rity, enjoy their brief span of fullest strength and completion, then as
quickly fade, so, in the heavens ruled by impatient, capricious gods,
the cycles hurry by. Proudly, disdainfully, Hina-in-the-Moon picks
her path through the mist of stars, sweeps up to the zenith, where she
pauses to pour down her liquid beauty upon the green-glossed fronds
of each coco palm and to admire her reflection in each stilled lagoon.
You are lovely, Hina . . . but enough! Move on. Give way to the
sun, which brave Maui once snared with a net of your flowing hair.
Tarry not, lest upward gazing man imagine time has stopped and himself become immortal, but hasten down the sky, reminding him that
his days are numbered and most fleeting. Hide your face, and let Mahana part the waters and burst upward in your place.

It was such a dawn that Rata and his weary crew witnessed on
the morning following the storm. The wind had died, the sea had
quieted. For a full hour Rata had paced the deck before the helm, chaf-
ing at the continuing darkness which held secret from him the where-
abouts of the remainder of his fleet. Surely they were there? Surely
they, too, somehow, had lived throughout the night? Twice he had had
the conch shells blown, and had remained motionless for minutes after-
ward, waiting for an answer however distant, however whisper-faint.
None came.

"But of course!" he said roughly. "They are light. The wind has carried them far. Yet they are there; they will make for us when their eyes can see." Hoa Pahi made no reply and the king whirled upon him. "Have you lost your tongue?" he demanded sharply. "Speak!"

"What is there to say?"

"Tell me that I am right, that it will be so!"

"Very well," said Hoa Pahi with a sigh, "I agree with you. Our kinsmen will set their course for us as soon as their eyes do see. But the dead, Rata, are sightless."

"The dead . . . ?"

"Yes."

"You hold no hope?" Rata asked, the flare of anger gone.

"My king," said the older man patiently, "you are still new to the sea and do not realize by how narrow a margin we ourselves are spared. The day will show us—nothing."

At this moment Hina stepped down from the sky and drew after her the trailing blue-black tresses of which the night is made. From east to west they swept as if at a toss of her siren head—tantalizing, illusive shadows which the sun unflaggingly pursues. The barren ocean was disclosed from rim to distant rim, empty, desolate, unbroken by hull or spar or sail. Slowly, paddlemen and warriors rose and scanned the now calmed and placid horizons. Then, still slowly, they resumed their places on the thwarts and took hold once more of the smooth-worn shafts of the paddles. When Rata climbed the rigging to wrap his arm about the masthead and search still farther, and when he came down to put his feet again upon the deck, no one looked up, no one spoke. No one needed to be told that in all the limitless expanse of the Pacific, Vaa-i-ama stood alone.

Rata cast a quick glance over his ship. She had not passed through the night unscathed. Lashings which held Tahua's small pandanus house had parted, and the structure slanted at such an angle that it was plain little more would have been required to wash it over the side. Deck planking between the two hulls had carried away, and, worst of all, the sail had torn from the boom and hung in tattered shreds. At sight of the useless sail the king paused and a frown creased his brow. Must he meet Pahua with but half a ship? He had counted on every bit of maneuverability that both wind and paddle could give. Well, it was done; there was no help for it.

Briskly he strode down the deck between the rows of his men.

Here and there he slapped a bronzed and naked back. "You, Taroa, and you, Timi! Get below, find tools and planking. Make right the decks! You, Mata, and you, Marau—get hawsers, bend them about the ark of Oro and clear away the remnants of the sail. You others! —Hau, Hema and Horo—light fires, bring food and drinking nuts to take the salt from out our mouths. We are living men, and we must eat, for there are battles still waiting to be fought!"

With lashing tongue and stinging, bracing blows from his open palm Rata roused his crew. For every man there was work to do and no time to think or mourn. When the war canoe rang with the sound of hammer blows, the thud of running feet, with shouts and calls, when smoke curled upward from between the stones in the sanded pit before the mast and the smell of roasting pork filled the air, when all was bustle and activity, Rata walked back the length of the fire-red ship to his station in the stern. Here Tavae and Hoa Pahi had brought aboard the steering oar and bent over it examining for flaw or strain. Squatting to one side, quietly contemplating the sea, was Tahua. He sat upon his heels in his customary posture, his chin supported on his knees and his bruised hands tucked under his armpits.

Rata dropped down beside him. "It is you, old man, we must thank for this morning."

The priest lifted his head and turned his small, cold eyes on the king. "Am I the creator of the day?"

"No; yet if it were not for you and your temple drum we would not be here to know and greet it."

"Again you are mistaken, Rata. The drum but called to Oro."

"Perhaps. But it called forth as well something from within ourselves. Beneath its spell we were for a short space of time not single, individual men, but an isolated storm-swept symbol of our race. Did you not feel it to be so?"

Tahua made a gesture as if he would brush Rata's thought aside, but in mid-air his hand came to an abrupt halt, then went back under his armpit. "I was about to deny the truth of what you say and to tell you that while I stood within the lurching, straining ark I was conscious only of Oro's nearness and nothing else. But I cannot." He smiled faintly and an unwonted warmth crept into his reedy voice. "I felt as you. We were neither pilot, paddleman, warrior, priest nor king, but a thing at once greater and simpler—Island Man. When you came upon

143

me I was still marveling that I should have plodded through such a long lifetime only now, almost at its close, to make such an elemental and uplifting discovery. Who knows? Perhaps it was the reason of my coming."

"Who knows?" Rata repeated. "But whatever the cause I am heartily glad that come you did."

Food was placed before them and soon Tavae and Hoa Pahi joined the circle.

"We have earned this meal," said Rata heartily. "Eat well, friends. Through the day we shall stand watches turn and turn about so that all may have the chance for sleep. If tomorrow we are to sight Pahua, every man must be refreshed."

Hoa Pahi reached for a steaming breadfruit and split it in two with thick, calloused hands. "If we had sail, tomorrow might well be the day for which we have planned so long." He snapped a piece of the breadfruit into his mouth, and for a moment his jaws worked silently. "With paddle alone it will take more than twice as long, and when we arrive many will be far from rested."

"Twice as long! Then we must have more at the paddles."

Hoa Pahi spoke seriously. "In so doing you would reduce our chances; chances which we must admit are none too bright in any case."

"I admit nothing of the sort," Rata said boldly, "and I cannot support delay!"

"Could we not make land and weave another sail?" Tavae inquired.

"And waste not one but half a dozen days?"

"You are our leader, Rata," the man from Huahine replied quietly, "and where you go I will follow. But it occurs to me that a day or two spent wisely now may add years to all our lives."

"That is sensibly said," the priest remarked, "and although I have few years to which to look forward, I am of the same mind."

"If my rudder is to have full command of Vaa-i-ama," Hoa Pahi added bluntly, "I must have a sail."

Rata had pushed away the food which lay before him. He could not but admit the soundness of his companions' advice, yet he made no reply, and at last Hoa Pahi looked up hoping to read the reason of his silence in the king's face. He discovered Rata staring off over the ship's bows as though he had completely forgotten the others and as if the subject of their discourse was quite gone from his mind. His eyes were bright, and the slight dilation of his nostrils betrayed an excitement for which Hoa Pahi could not immediately account, although he twisted his head and gazed over his shoulder to follow Rata's glance. He saw only the tranquil ocean unmarred by so much as leaping dolphin or skittering minnows. The sky above was equally uninteresting. Save one small black cloud which hung suspended in the middle distance, nothing met the eye but the clear, limpid blueness which always succeeds a night of rain. Experienced mariner that he was, Hoa Pahi read no sign of danger or adventure of any sort. Still puzzled, he turned back to the king.

"What is it, Rata, that you . . . ?" He got no farther.

Rata leaped up and shouted, "You shall have it! You shall have your sail and it will be no dead and lifeless thing of matting. We shall put *wings* to Vaa-i-ama!"

Wings! An idea suddenly entered Hoa Pahi's head and he swung around to look again, intently this time, at the single small, dark cloud which he had seen. It appeared more black than before, nearer, more distinct. He made it out for what it was. The dreaded bird-fiend, plunderer of the ships of men, came on with slow-beating pinions, and beneath it dark riffles spread across the sea.

With a growl, Hoa Pahi struggled to his feet. "Sails, you say? I see nothing here but a vicious marauder who strikes in safety from the air to seize a man in his talons and bear him away to some foul and never discovered nest!" He grasped Rata's shoulder. "Get below! It is kings and chiefs he seeks, not common men. Hide yourself!"

"Do you jest? Safe I should certainly be by skulking out of sight if the creature prefers the flesh of rulers, for in so doing I would cast off the last vestiges of kingship. I think it better that you lift me up to meet this demon bird."

"Lift—? Now it is you who jest." Hoa Pahi called down the ship, "Spears! Spears, all of you, and prepare to protect the king!"

"Put them down," Rata commanded as men tumbled over each other to get at their weapons. "Lay down your arms! Remain quiet. Hoa Pahi, though affection be the cause, forgets himself when he thus carelessly flings orders right and left. This winged beast hunts me alone. Then leave to me the pleasure of dragging its carcass from the skies. Stand at your posts and do not interfere. Perhaps you will soon see that this fresh danger is but an answer to our greatest need."

Hoa Pahi appeared on the verge of mutiny. The blood vessels along his neck and the smaller veins on his forehead stood out as if they were near to bursting, and his chest heaved convulsively. "Do not expose yourself, Rata," he exploded, "you have not the right to take such risk!"

Rata shot a look upward at the fast-approaching bird. In the distance it had appeared to hover low over the water, but by now all could see that in truth it flew at a great height and directly for Vaa-i-ama.

"There will be less risk, Hoa Pahi," said Rata, "if you will stop your useless protests and give me your attention. For I must have help." He beckoned to the man of Huahine. "Yours also, Tavae."

Quickly the king outlined his plan; then, to the amazement of the watching crew, he seized his spear with its long, double-edged row of saw-like shark teeth, jumped to the ship's rail and dove into the sea. His head broke the surface close to the end of the steering oar. He had wrapped his left arm over the wide blade, hugging it to his side, when a dark shadow passed across the ship, causing all eyes to swing up and discover the bird blotting out the sun with its extended wings directly overhead. With long neck, naked of plumage, craned downward and sharp-curved beak agape, it deliberately examined through eyes jet-black and unblinking each man upon the deck. About the central pylon of the mast it wheeled, wings rigid and unmoving, looking—looking for its especial prey.

Rata raised his burnished spear. "Now, Hoa Pahi! Now, Tavae!"

Together the two men standing in the stern of the war canoe threw their weight upon the tiller. Like a giant seesaw the end to which Rata clung was wrenched from out the sea. Up it rocketed till the king was almost on a level with the masthead, yet far abaft and far beyond all aid. In mid-air he dangled, small-seeming against the hovering, circling shadow.

"Come!" Rata challenged. "Come, fiend that sullies the clean skies, here is a prize to carry to your skull-lined nest!"

The wings folded and the bird dove straight for the man at the paddle's end. With a whistling rush such as the sea makes spouting through a narrow cleft in coral reefs, it plummeted for the outstretched human bait while all of Rata's men stared in mounting horror. Less than a ship's length separated their king from the demoniac feathered thing, when suddenly the two black wings shot out, breaking the lightning fall. The bird rocked back, head flung skyward, feet stabbing out with curling claws wide spread, reaching to sink in Rata's flesh.

"Down with him!" Hoa Pahi cried, his courage, boundless when he himself was threatened, failing at sight of Rata's peril.

"But," the bewildered Tavae protested, "did you not hear . . . ?"

"Down with him!" Hoa Pahi bellowed, and he heaved up on the helm with such force that Tavae, still unprepared, was lifted bodily from the deck. Rata went down, and so swiftly that a geyser rose where he disappeared beneath the protecting sea, yet not so swiftly that the clutching talons of the infuriated bird failed to graze his shoulders and stain with scarlet the waters that closed above his head.

A piercing, ear-splitting screech came from the throat of the baffled bird as with frantically beating wings it sought to rise for another dive upon its victim. But its upward flight was lumbering slow, and before it was many feet above the sea Hoa Pahi and Tavae bore down again upon their catapult so that Rata burst up into the sunlight with the salt brine running from him in flashing rivulets.

"Strike! Strike now!"

Hoa Pahi's exhortation was unneeded. Rata's arm snapped back and the great spear slashed out in a sweeping arc. The jagged, firm-studded rows of sharks' teeth whipped across the bird's right wing close to the body, severing it at a single thrust. This time the scream which rent the air was one, not of rage, but of anguished pain, and it rose still higher when Rata stabbed once again to deal with the second pinion as he had the first; it continued as the creature's body fell twisting over and over to plunge at last into the ocean. Then it was stilled, and never was heard again. Gently dipping and turning like giant purau leaves making a leisurely descent to earth, the two wings fluttered slowly down to settle one on either side of Vaa-i-ama. Rata slid along the still up-slanting steering oar and dropped to the deck.

"There are your sails. Draw them in, rig them to the mast and we shall fly!" Many hands reached over the sides and raised the massed feathers of glossy, shining black. After watching a moment Rata confronted his helmsman. His face clouded. "Now, Hoa Pahi, perhaps you will explain yourself. I gave you orders to hold me up aloft. Do you think it seemly that your king should retreat so precipitately before an enemy? And what do you mean by giving me such a thorough ducking?"

"I see no objection to giving ground if it is but to attain a victory."

"Is that any reason to cause me to pop in and out of the sea like a crab which a child dangles on the end of a stick?"

"Why, Rata," said Hoa Pahi with exaggerated innocence, "you must not hold Tavae and myself to blame if we lost our footing. Remember that yours is the weight of three and that we are but two ordinary men."

The king was ready with an abrupt retort, but just then the crew heaved on the sennit lines, the feathered sails rose up and caught the wind. Far to port and starboard they stretched, no longer menacing but darkly, majestically beautiful in the attitude of soaring flight. Vaa-i-ama's bows rose high, and lighter, more fleet than ever before she skimmed forward over the shining waves. Suddenly Hoa Pahi found his hands full with the leaping tiller.

Rata turned to him with the look of laughter bright in his eyes. "You are a very great pilot, Friend-of-the-Ship—and also a very great liar."

XXIII

CERTAIN calms may be far more forbidding than the worst of storms. There are dead and doldrum calms which bring home to a man more strongly than all else the immensity and the vast, apathetic unconcern of the ocean world. "What," the torpid waters seem to say, "does a ship pass here, a ship whose people live in hope to see again the port from which they sailed? Do they pray for wind? Well, no matter! Perhaps the breeze will come, perhaps not. Perhaps they will return, and again—perhaps not. It is of no consequence." Such is the feeling which a sleeping sea may inspire, and so it was with those aboard Vaa-i-ama on the day following the encounter with the demon-bird. A film of gray was spread throughout the sky, and as the hours passed it darkened so that the ship floated in a strange half-light which was like neither night nor day. As the sky slowly changed to deeper and deeper shades of gray, so did the sea.

They were alike both in color and in their absolute passivity, and it was impossible to tell where one ended and the other began. The men stared about them trying to distinguish a horizon-line, but there was none to be seen, and at last, blinking and bemazed, they would turn back to gaze at near-by objects on the ship itself: at rising shrouds, at bailing-shells or at each other as if to make certain that the all-pervading grayness was not the color of total blindness.

"We are near," said Hoa Pahi. "I have not forgotten this overcast thick as marsh fog or breath of whales."

"And the atolls?" Rata demanded. Both had spoken in voices hushed as though they stood within a marae. In such an utter, waiting stillness, to speak aloud, each felt, would be to be heard league upon league.

"We shall raise them," Hoa Pahi answered quietly. "And soon."

"Good. I am ready."

"You have a plan?"

Rata lifted the heavy battle axe which rested against the gunwale at his side. He ran a finger over the long, sharpened edge. "A plan? Yes. It is simple: to attack!"

"Of course. But . . ."

"That is all. Others who have been devoured by Pahua spent their entire strength in trying to avoid it, to draw away to safety. We have not come looking for safety, and we shall waste not a paddle stroke in attempting to escape. It may be, Hoa Pahi, that in ages to come other evils will sit astraddle the world as does Pahua today, and if that is so men will then go out to do battle as we do now. Whether they will remember us, who can say? But if they do let it be told that we rode into Pahua with all the might we had and that we came not out again till it was destroyed."

"May it be so, Rata," the other replied soberly, and then he raised his arm. He pointed off to starboard. "There it lies."

Rata looked. Where a moment before had been only gray emptiness an ugly bulge was now visible on the horizon. Still distant and blurred, its color seemed little different from the leaden sky and sea; yet Rata knew that it was neither air nor water at which he gazed but something massed and solid. "You have done well, Hoa Pahi," he said calmly. "Once I said to you that you had lived to guide me. You have done so and I am grateful. Bring the ship about, good friend."

The helmsman took a step to one side and drew the tiller after him. To the even stroke of the paddles, Vaa-i-ama described a quarter circle on the sullen, unmoving and dusky breast of the sea till the twin godheads at the bows pointed straight for Pahua. The paddlemen who for

long hours had swung their blades in a strange, numbed torpor now lifted their heads. What meant this change of course? They turned to peer over their shoulders at the king, who stood with Tavae and Hoa Pahi upon the steering platform. Nothing was to be read upon their faces, yet there may have been a certain fixity in the way each of the three men stared stonily ahead and also a slight tightening of the muscles about their jaws and lips. Several dropped their paddles for an instant to stand and scan the path before them, then took their places while others rose to do the same. A murmuring hum passed over the vessel and it swelled and grew as the realization sank within them that this was journey's end, this the day for which was all the sweat and toil of preparation, this the hour for which Vaa-i-ama had been made and launched, this the moment, it might be, for which each one of them had been born. Among them, the king included, were men of barely twenty; others, like Hoa Pahi, were in their middle years, and there was Tahua, whose age was such that he himself could not readily give its measure. Yet there was no one, either young or old, who had not found life in the island now left far behind a thing both pleasant and desirable. So, too, there was no one now who failed to wonder briefly and to ask himself: have I seen all the days which the gods have granted, and is this the last? Is this dim twilight which hangs so heavily to be followed by a darkness which never ends? Have I looked for the last time on high Tahiti with all its wonders, its mysteries and its beauty? Still the paddles did not pause, but rose and fell, driving Vaa-i-ama steadily on length by length, mile by mile toward the hulking shape of Pahua, where alone the questioning thoughts would find an answer.

"When you rode my father's ship, Hoa Pahi," Rata asked, "at what distance were you from Pahua when the valves began to open?"

"We were near," he replied. "No more than a mile away."

"And what do you judge the distance which lies between us now?"

"At three miles, perhaps more. But we are seen already, make no doubt."

"I have felt for some time as if it were so, but it seems to me unreasonable. Is this monster possessed of eyes?"

"Not as we know them, Rata. But surely when you have fished you have passed your spear before a tridacna clam. Have you not noticed how, at the mere shadow of a movement, it will snap its jaws? You could say that it has a thousand eyes, for the curled flesh of the lips is sensitive to light from end to end."

"Let the number of its eyes be told by tens of thousands. It is all the same to us. Unlike other ships which have passed this way, we come *wanting* to be seen. Ihu-ata's elves did not give my war canoe its coat of flame that it should hide or cringe. Let Pahua squat gloating in his watery lair; we shall not disappoint him, neither shall we flail this sea of rank odor in an effort to get away." Rata clapped a hand on Hoa Pahi's shoulder. "Whatever comes he shall think he has swallowed an army of scorpions."

He leaped down to the rowing deck and strode quickly to the mast. Between the black, slumbering wings he climbed till he reached the top of the tall spar and there he clung while with his keen, dark eyes he looked out on the still-motionless, dumbly threatening thing which lay wedged between two small palm-dotted islets. Had Hoa Pahi once spoken of the breath of evil? Rata felt that even if he had been ignorant of what he witnessed, the awareness of impending danger would have been as real. It was danger in which all the lesser dangers, all the smaller evils which dog man's footsteps in a bewildering world, were merged in a single monstrous power before which no king had ever seemed a king. You are terrible, Pahua, he thought, because only a fraction of your looming bulk is living creature, the rest unfeeling stone-hard, stone-cold weight of shell. Sluggish life stirs there within you and a blind, devouring urge will open cavern-wide your mouth. But it is the insensate movement of a mountain which in roaring avalanche crushes the village at its feet. You are every destructive soulless force in all this universe before which we have blanched and quailed. Your ugly shadow falls on these blue seas, and the gray fear of you reaches out to haunt the farthest island. But were we made to exist at your mindless whim alone? That I do not believe, and so Vaa-i-ama stands on to meet you!

Already he could see the wave-like valleys in the mollusc's husk. Beginning shallow and crowded near the rounded dome, they then rayed out, deepening as they descended to end at the water's edge in high, vaulted arches rimmed with animal flesh of gleaming blue. Even as Rata watched, the smaller, knife-sharp circling ridges with which the shell was scored came into view. Across each rising mound and dipping slope they went as though ground out by a giant comb. All measured, all symmetrical, all precise, all unnaturally and chillingly exact. There was no flaw, no slightest blemish in the clam's tremendous armament. Through the entire southern seas no other thing existed so ideally suited, so inhumanly perfected, for the sole purpose of annihilation.

Perhaps it was appreciation of this sinister fact smiting Rata with sudden force; perhaps it was sheer bravado in the face of overwhelming odds or perhaps it was done for the effect upon his followers. Whatever the reason, a peal of laughter crashed from Rata's lips and fell upon the occupants of the war canoe with the jarring abruptness of a thunder clap. If Pahua had given voice the result could not have been more startling. Laughter!—at such a time and such a place? Laughter, in the midst of this enfolding murk of dull gray dusk, in the midst of this suspended silence pregnant with the sense of doom? It rang out clear and unabashed, mocking, defiant, and it shattered the pervading stillness as a knife of stone smashes the brittle shell of a coconut. All eyes turned upward to see the king outlined against the glowering sky. With long legs wrapped about the mast he leaned far out and forward. His fist was raised.

"Pahua!" he cried. "Does a heart beat in that hollowed mountain? Then open to us, for we have come to cut it out! Do you still clutch the bones of brave men in your cold embrace? Then open, for we have come to their rescue! Does stygian night lie foul and thick within? Then open, for my Ship of Flame will burn and cleanse! Spread, interlocking jaws! Unfold, swing down and up on slime-greased hinges, sweep wide and let the chasm yawn, for we have come to conquer and to slay!"

"To conquer! To slay!" Like an echo to Rata's own the shout rose up from the decks below. Two hundred men who a moment before were held benumbed and semi-paralyzed had jumped to their feet. The unhealthy spell of dread which had gripped them fell away under the war cry of their king, and spears whirled in the air above their heads.

"Come down, Rata," Hoa Pahi bellowed more loudly than all the others. "We hunger to do battle!"

Rata slid to the deck and looked with satisfaction at the eager faces which swarmed about him. Gone was all sign of lethargy, all sign of gloom or doubt. Eyes were bright, heads high. He sprang to his place beside the helmsman and his orders came sharp and fast.

"Trim sails! The wind will come when Pahua swallows half the sky. Stand by with bailing shells and gourds! The waters will boil when Pahua reaches for his prey. Lay your spears beside you and hold firmly to the paddles! The sea will race for Pahua when he stirs, but we must go still faster."

Tavae of Huahine came forward. "I, too, shall take a spear."

"No," Rata replied, "you are an archer and as such we need you. Take arrows from my quiver. Bind them three together so they may be triply strong. To their butts make fast a length of cordage, then fit them to my bow. Work quickly, for you shall soon find the target."

"I am willing but I am no giant. Never shall I be able to draw such a bow."

A smile flickered over Rata's lips. "So I once thought myself. But you will find, when the test comes, that you have strength of which you never dreamed. Full drawn or not, it will suffice, but hasten!"

Without further words, Tavae ran to carry out the king's command, and Rata was left alone with his pilot. Steadily the ship moved on through the somber, melancholy twilight, through the stagnant, breathless calm, making hardly a ripple on the listless sea. Little more than a mile away loomed the harsh, barren crust of Pahua, still dormant, ever dourly threatening with a menace which had frozen many another crew in helpless impotence.

The haft of Rata's great battle axe rested in his right hand. Slowly he swung it back and forth with his eyes on the moving blade of black volcanic rock. "The minutes are hurrying away from us, Hoa Pahi. They slip swiftly through our fingers and we cannot hold them back."

Hoa Pahi nodded gravely. "The next paddle stroke may well mark the last."

"There is something I would say while there is yet time."

Loudly the helmsman cleared his throat. "Yes, Rata."

"We are warriors, you and I; we are Tahitian men. And we conduct ourselves according to the laws and tapus of our people. Most of those customs I find good, but some, and one in particular, seem to me most needless. Why must we pretend to be without emotions? Are women alone capable of deep affection? Is it weakness in a man? It does not seem to me to be so, and for that reason I must speak before it is too late. I have been happy in my short lifetime because of the thing called friendship which has grown and lived between us. It has warmed my heart and it gives me courage so that even Pahua appears less formidable. But enough said. I simply wished that you should know."

Hoa Pahi's sight fogged and an unaccustomed huskiness was in his voice. "I am not like most others of our race: words do not, as you know, fall easily from my tongue. But . . ."

Rata looked up as the other hesitated. Their eyes met and locked. "But believe me," Hoa Pahi finished, "my feeling is the same."

The king's teeth flashed in a broad smile, and he brought the axe-head down on the deck with a resounding thump. "Thank you, Friend-of-the-Ship! Now you may bring us to grips with our enemy."

"You will use the axe?"

"Yes. Spears may goad and sting Pahua but they will not kill."

A dismal, long-protracted sigh struck their ears, and Hoa Pahi said quickly, "Take it up in both your hands, for that is the call of destiny."

XXIV

THE SOUND seemed to come not from a particular direction but from all directions, as if the sea itself stirred in uneasy slumber. But no man asked what was this awakening, nor what was the moaning, in-drawn breath; all knew. Pahua moved! There was a change in the fiercely jagged shore line. The wave-shaped lips of vivid blue now held between them a dark serpent where from end to end of the tridacna a narrow strip of the black interior was exposed. It was a serpent which slowly expanded, slowly lost the intensity of its color, graying as the upper shell rocked back and the pale light of day seeped in. Then it was gone and in its place was a widening arch with hanging, serrate edge and each curved scallop a dripping fang. To itself Pahua drew all things. The valve above sucked hungrily at the air, the valve below, dipping to a distant bottom, dragged after it the sea. As if a restraining dam had been brushed aside, the quiet waters on which the war canoe had rested burst smoking forward and the spreading wings were filled with a wind which shrieked like the fiendish bird from which they came. Rotating on an unseen axis, the entire surface of the ocean swerved up behind and down before. Vaa-i-ama was tilted at an angle which could have been no sharper had she been careening headlong over the slopes of Orofena. With a tug that threatened to tear the mast from its anchorage in the ship's bowels, the great black sails took hold. Straining and quivering, their impulse for flight unleashed and whipped to sudden life, they lifted Rata's valiant craft till her twin hulls barely skimmed the seething brine and rocketed her to apparent doom at a pace more swift than man in all history had ever traveled. And yet Rata cried again and again, "Faster! Faster! Faster!" until the blades of his rows of paddlemen flashed in and out with a lightning speed.

Had a minute passed? The distance was cut in half. In towering grandeur the shell rolled back and upward, higher and still higher into the clouded heavens. The roughness of its weathered outer crust passed from sight and exposed the cold, frightening beauty held within. No man had ever spoken of the huge clam's wondrous radiance, of its luster or its stunning splendor, for these things were hidden from all save those

156

about to die. But now, careless of its jealous secret, Pahua showed its wetly glistening face to Rata and his band. A gasp of amazement and of momentary unreasoning despair escaped those who from their racing ship watched the opened shell catch on its flaring expanse the dim obscurity of that somber, fatal day and fling it back illumined with a brilliance of its own. Beauty, yes—such as neither Rata nor any other had ever seen, but holding something hideous as well. Was it that a man, breathing his last remaining breaths, discovered in its polished surface the sunlight as he had often seen it when diving beneath a green lagoon? Was it that he saw there Hina's silver sheen, the shimmering whiteness of oval-petaled tiare, the flickering rose of clustered coral, the tremulous blue of midday sky—and so touched final black despond? Perhaps. For all there was of color and loveliness in every land or sea found an iridescent reflection in the burnished mother-of-pearl with which Pahua's gigantic shell was sheathed.

"Steady on!" Rata shouted. "Be not deceived by a mirage of false beauty. It is death at which you stare! Stroke, warriors, stroke and cast the sea away behind! Carry us where we may shower blows numerous as falling drops of rain!"

Had Vaa-i-ama ridden the roiled gray waters without paddle or sail she would still have hurtled into the abyss as tempestuously as if she plunged over the falls of Ihu-ata. She was one with the hurrying torrent, one with flying scud and howling wind. But the flashing paddles sent her even more rapidly than these. To right and left the blade of Hoa Pahi's steering oar cut into the tumbling wake, holding the ship to a course which led into the tridacna where it gaped the widest. There, at dead center, rose a mighty column of purest white. Its base, fastened to the sunken lower valve, was lost to sight, but above, it reached up to the glazed overhanging roof, spread across the domed shell like the creeping roots of an inverted banyan tree. It might have been the stone pillar of investiture, the pillar before which Tahua made Rata king, grown to enormous size; it might have been the Moi turned to shining alabaster. But it was neither. It was solid, fibrous muscle; the muscle, now nearly full extended, which, once Vaa-i-ama was well within, would contract to draw closed the yawning jaws, to shut the frightful trap.

"Aim for it!" Rata barked close to Hoa Pahi's ear. "That is our goal. Never swerve; let nothing turn us aside. We must wedge it between the prows. Tavae will help."

"Tavae . . . ?"

"You will see!" He grasped Tavae, who stood ready with the bow, and, still clutching his battle axe in his right hand, started down the ship, drawing the archer with him. Between the double rows of sweating paddlemen they lurched forward across the heaving deck. Past the snapping, groaning mast bent like a wand of aeho cane in mountain wind, past the sanded fire-pit, past the rattling, thrashing pandanus of the ark of Oro they fought their way into the vessel's bows, where the carved figureheads still pointed skyward with a brave air of invincibility. Here no planking ran across the hulls, and Tavae, standing to starboard, was separated from the king by a six-foot gap through which the ocean sluiced churning between the two halves of the ship.

"On your knees, Tavae!" Rata called, and with outstretched arm he pointed to the sand-white column about whose base the surf leaped high. "Drive there your arrows and drive them deep! Then heave yourself upon a line; cast others to the crew. Bring me where my axe can bite and gouge and sever, for that is the heart of Pahua!"

Rata's Ship of Flame passed beneath the jutting blue-rimmed brow and shot into the walled inferno where whirled the caged wind and sea in unholy, clashing strife. There came a sudden baffled roar from Hoa Pahi as the war canoe ploughed into the twisting currents and swerved sharply from its path.

Rata leaned toward the man from Huahine. "Now! Let fly!"

Ready crouching, Tavae sent one bolt after another into the white trunk, and the coiled lines hissed over the gunwales. A half dozen of the crew jumped to seize the sennit cords and together tugged and pulled, warping Vaa-i-ama back to her course. Hand over hand they hove in the lines and the valiant ship drove on. With a shock that threw men sprawling on the decks and that would have sent both king and archer overboard had they not clung to the projecting stems, she rammed the upright pillar squarely between the bows and so held fast. In the next instant paddles were thrown down and spears by the hundreds whistled through the air. Like the quills of the sea porcupine, they protruded everywhere from Pahua's bloodless flesh. Did they wound? Were they more than the annoying pricks of so many swarming gnats? No man could tell, for Pahua had no voice other than that of the

elements which had stormed in through the open portals. And now that the grim stone gates stood wide to their full extent even those sounds fast died away. The turmoil gave way to a second calm. Yet how different from that through which they had passed while still free upon the ocean! Lowering that had been, threatening and sinister. But this was the quiet of the grave. This was the calm that comes when all is done and the last word has been spoken; this was the beginning of eternity. With no missile or spear left unthrown, all but one of the many warriors of Tahiti stood silent with empty hands. A trembling ran through the length of the gallant ship, a trembling which it caught from the smooth round shaft against which it lay. The shell began to close. Again there rose a low, keening wail as the air stirred, pressing to escape to the boundless world without. But at the same time a hoarse bellow came from a human throat. Back and forth between the imprisoning walls it rocked, deep-toned as the greatest drum of Oro.

"O Rata!" boomed Hoa Pahi as once before in a mountain glen, *"lay on!"*

And standing as he had done at the foot of the Moi with legs braced wide apart, Rata swung the battle axe high above his head. With a twist of his body, a swing of broad shoulders, a sweep of long, sinewy arms, a final flex of powerful wrists, he whipped down the black basaltic blade with a force so terrific that it sank clear to the shaft in the monster's flesh. Like twin snakes, two segments were torn loose from the central mass of muscle, one to lash briefly on the dark surface of the water, then lie flaccid and still, the other to shrink writhing, withering toward the slowly, implacably descending vault.

"That, Pahua," Rata cried, "for Tehe who died in my father's ship!" He wrenched free the mighty axe and once more it swung on high. "Ho, Pahua! Do you recall Toma who then paddled bow?" Down whirled the murderous blade. "There—he rises to smite anew! And Teva who was so young—will you feel the weight of his vengeful spirit?" The axe which had conquered a Moi spun through the air and slashed again. Ever faster, with ever mounting fury Rata hewed while he tolled the names of the honored, still-mourned dead. "This for Peti who leaped the highest; this for Tau of big ears; this for Hei who forever sang; this for Hema who dove the deepest! For Horo, reader of the stars, for Ata who loved to laugh, for Manea, for Manua, Noa and Otai!"

The blows rained down, and all about Vaa-i-ama floated, like pale repellent worms the sun had never touched, the coiling strands of muscle which Rata hacked away. But the light was fading fast. Half cut through, the remaining close-compacted tendons continued to contract, and though Rata poured out his strength, his sorrow and his anger without stint and without reserve, he failed to halt the grim, tightening embrace of the closing valves, he failed to arrest the falling night, failed to stay the approach of suffocating death. The warriors stared at the ruthlessly approaching nacreous dome above; they stared at the inexorably narrowing road behind. There was no outcry, no lament. They waited quietly as men have always done when faced with malevolent power which surpasses the understanding and the ability of mortal hands to combat.

Yet one among them was no common man. One was king, but more than that: a giant king whose wish for superhuman strength and stature was both heard and granted. Now with Oro's gift he labored; but there were limits to the endurance of even the great Rata. His heavy breathing filled the darkening cavern; the names of the departed still rang out, echoing hollowly as if he shouted down an endless tunnel to Te Po. The axe rose and fell, still slashing deep, but less swiftly than before.

At last Rata paused. He glanced once at the gruesome intermeshing jaws where a strip of the day's light showed so narrow that he could have spanned it with his aching arms. Then he faced again the muscled pillar. It was no longer so monstrous large. Indistinct in the dense gloom, its girth appeared no greater than Rata's own. Gathering all his remaining forces, he lifted the battle axe and brought it down with such impact that it sent a shudder through the length of the canoe.

"That, Pahua, for Rai whose lips clung to his beloved's, for Tani whom his sister mourns!"

The shell-hard teeth of the tridacna ground together, snapped shut in a vise-like grip, and in utter, impenetrable blackness Rata raised once more his fire-toughened blade. "Take this to your vitals, thing accursed!" His voice rolled like captive thunder in the thick, oppressive night. *"It is the liberating blow of Tumu-nui!"*

There was a whirr in the close, fetid air, followed by the sound of ripping, tearing flesh. About the sealed entrance waves leapt and splashed. Pahua's cruel lips fell apart—not with measured, contemptuous pace—but abruptly, in a dying spasm. The scalloped mouth gaped half open and moved no more. Light flooded in and disclosed Rata leaning heavily on the handle of his battle axe. Before him rose no tall column, no white pillar, no bulk of drawing muscle. The stroke for Tumunui had driven through; and upon the shadowed waters Vaa-i-ama drifted free.

They did not shout, they did not cheer. Still half dazed, men picked up their paddles, and Hoa Pahi guided the ship in where the pearl-gray roof sloped down to touch the sea. There, amid disintegrating timbers, lay the remains of those who had passed that way before. Carefully their bones were gathered up and placed within the house of Oro in Tahua's watchful care.

Rata stepped up beside his helmsman. The war canoe was brought about, and now the paddles moved with increasing vigor. Out of the gloom of dank, cold walls, beneath the frowning arch of shell Vaa-i-ama sped—out onto the broad, untrammeled ocean where a fresh salt breeze plucked at the winged sail.

"What course shall I set?" the pilot inquired.

Rata smiled. "Need you ask? Make for an island where lagoons are broad and clear, where shelving beaches sparkle white, where mountains climb above all others and slopes are clothed with green. Make for an island where food is sweet and plentiful, where there is time for love and song and laughter, where friends abound and life is fair."

"Very well," said Hoa Pahi, "I shall point the bows for high Tahiti!"

From the direction in which they had come there suddenly arose a sound like the blowing of a school of whales. All turned; all looked. There, not far astern, were two small atolls with their circling ring of palms. But the forbidding mass which had bridged between was gone, and where it once had crouched there stretched open water, a channel which still boiled and eddied where the monster sank forever beneath the waves. Only now, so it seemed, did the magnitude of their victory dawn upon the many watchers. Only now were they able fully to grasp the significance of what had happened. Pahua was no more! Never again would he plague the island world. Pahua was dead—swept away, destroyed by island men and an island king, great Rata of Tahiti.

All his men found voice at once, and a deafening roar burst from their throats. Hoa Pahi gave a tremendous heave upon his steering oar, swinging it up from the crotch in which it rested and lifting it high above his head. All smaller paddles were in the air as well, and the din was such that it must have come near to reaching those who waited on the distant shore to which the voyagers made their way.

"Maeva Arii—Hail King! Hail!—Hail!—Hail!"

EPILOGUE

TETUA'S TALE IS DONE—*a tale known and told from one end to the other of the largest of all oceans. It might have come from the lips of a man of the dangerous Tuamotus, from an Hawaiian or from a tattooed Maori of New Zealand. In any case it would have been much the same. Not every island bard, however, holds the awareness that it is Rata and Turia of Tahiti he must thank for the gift of life. This Tetua knows. For Rata came safely to his homeland and safely to his love. There were children—many children—quite as they had wished, and the same blood which filled the veins of Pahua's conqueror now courses, still lustily, in Tetua's own.*

Do not ask him of Rata's end, for, in his firm opinion, the famous king has never died. Impelled by the restlessness which made of his race the greatest navigators and explorers of all time, he made many another voyage until a day at last came when he sailed never to return. Tetua insists that he is still at sea, that for hundreds of years, and even to the present, mariners have glimpsed his winged Ship of Flame in the hazy distance. If one believes that the noble deeds of those who have gone before live after them like beckoning shadows luring others on in emulation, then what he says is very true. Certain it is, at least, that so long as one man of Polynesia holds within his mind the story of the valiant warrior—so long will Rata, too, endure.

But now the day is far spent and our canoe waits beneath the purau tree. Tetua will lend a hand in the launching, and it will be a hand firm and brown like Rata's own. He will wave in farewell, then walk back to the house which clings solitary and small upon the great curving strand. Perhaps a backward glance will seem to show him a lonely figure of a man with no company other than the near-by sea, the winds and moun-

164

EPILOGUE

tains. But no; we may continue untroubled on our way to the pleasant, uninspired comfort of men who live in crowds. Tetua, whose proud head is the abode of heroes, feels no slightest lack and would never think to follow in our cluttered paths.

Yet a welcome is waiting there by the splendid bay of Matavai if one should seek it out again.

THE END

PRINTER'S NOTE

The type in which the text of the book is set is Original Old Style. It is based on an English old face of the late Caslon period, and was cut for Linotype some three decades ago, being derived particularly from a font issued by the A. D. Farmer & Son foundry of New York in the middle of the last century.

The letterpress portion of this book and the binding are by the Kingsport Press, Inc., Kingsport, Tennessee. The illustrations were printed in sheet-fed gravure by the Beck Engraving Company of Philadelphia and New York. The book has been designed by James Hendrickson.